Sheila

Weekly Reader

Children's Book Club

EDUCATION CENTER • COLUMBUS 16, OHIO

Presents

ISLAND BOY

BY *Robert R. Harry, sr.*

ISLAND
BOY

A Story of Ancient Hawaii

ILLUSTRATED BY *Reisie Lonette*

NEW YORK, N. Y.

LOTHROP, LEE & SHEPARD CO., INC.

WEEKLY READER

Children's Book Club

Edition, 1957

This book
is affectionately dedicated
to Dorothy May, without whose love and loyalty
Paulo's story would never
have been written.

CONTENTS

CHAPTER:

Special Notice to Book Club Members

★ This book is a selection of the WEEKLY READER CHILDREN'S BOOK CLUB. It was chosen especially for our members by the Weekly Reader Selection Board after careful consideration of hundreds of other books for girls and boys.

Members of the WEEKLY READER CHILDREN'S BOOK CLUB receive six or more exciting books during the year — including one or more Free Bonus Books upon joining. They also receive a Membership Certificate, Club Bookmarks and regular Book Club Bulletins.

We hope you enjoy this book. Your friends will enjoy it, too. If they are not already members, why not ask them to join the WEEKLY READER CHILDREN'S BOOK CLUB.

WEEKLY READER
Children's Book Club
EDUCATION CENTER, COLUMBUS 16, OHIO

ISLAND BOY

CHAPTER ONE

The Last Survivor

SEVEN times the silver moon of harvest had dipped into the black sea since his mother and all the others were killed. Now Paulo trembled, thinking of the warriors who had come from the North and struck in the darkest hour of the night. All evening before their attack, the elders of the village had argued in the council house. The strange warriors had shouted their demands angrily. Paulo, like the other children, sat at the edge of the crowd and listened.

"You must pay tribute to our new chief!" a red-faced warrior shouted.

But Paulo's poor village had nothing to satisfy these strangers.

Rains on this island of Maui had been scanty for some time. The taro crop was so poor the villagers could make only enough poi for immediate needs. And pounded taro root for poi was their daily bread. Smoke houses were almost empty of jerked meat.

Even the coconut crop was small and nets came in with scanty hauls of fish.

How then, could these people pay taxes to a strange chief?

The villagers trembled in the face of the warrior's wrath. Creeping away by twos and threes, they hid in grass huts and hollow places in the cliffs.

This was a peaceful village in ancient Hawaii. None knew how to make war. That was the business of the royal ones, the kings and chiefs.

With fire torches to light the scene in dead of night, the strange warriors destroyed Paulo's village. Probing spears and sharp stone hatchets grew bloody. It was death for any man, woman or child they caught. The warriors were relentless in their cruel search.

Possessions of the villagers were scattered and bodies crushed like eggs in a nest torn by great claws of manu pueo, the owl from thunder mountain.

It was indeed a terrible night.

As the angry disk of the morning sun grew red through a haze of smoke, Paulo gradually realized he was the only one left living. Stunned by this knowledge and desperately afraid, for six whole days and nights the boy huddled in a secret cave behind the village. A small boy's cave, not easily found.

For food, Paulo nibbled shreds of dried fish and almost rancid poi. He had no drinking water but the rains, which came after the fire.

On the morning of the seventh day of loneliness, Paulo awoke from restless sleep to see a man moving cautiously across the distant beach. A large outrigger canoe was dragged high up on the sand. Its crab-claw sail flapped loosely in the breeze like a tired beast of burden, panting for its second wind. Paulo hardly dared to move as he watched with fear and trembling.

When his sleepy eyes grew stronger against the sun's glare, he recognized the stranger as the slim one, Boki the trader.

Paulo's shout was a wail of relief. "Boki, Boki!" he called. "Over here!"

The man turned from his scrutiny of the ruined village and motioned with a wave of his hand.

Paulo hurried to the beach. His arms encircled the trader's waist in a passionate embrace.

Long minutes passed as, wordlessly, the man patted the boy's slender shoulders. Together, they looked over the ruins. Both could see there was nothing to be done.

"Go to the canoe, little one!" the trader said, softly.

The man's voice sounded hoarse. Paulo knew that Boki also was afraid. Yet the trader lingered for a last look around as though saying goodbye to familiar faces and scenes he was still seeing in his mind, but would not see again. Boki lived by trading native goods from one island to another. Lone traders like him were the only regular travelers between the Pacific islands before the white man came. He had made many friends.

When Paulo reached the canoe he turned to wait for Boki. He was afraid to take his eyes from the man, finding it hard to believe that help had come at last. He saw the trader stoop to lift a charred package wrapped in kapa cloth. With this in his hand, Boki joined the boy at the canoe. Paulo did not even wonder what had been found worth saving.

They both jumped aboard as a rolling swell caught the stern and, receding, dragged the outrigger afloat.

Gradually, the green shore became one with emerald water. Brisk trade winds filled the crab-claw sail. Muscles corded as Boki strained at the short steering paddle. He picked up an extra paddle and gave it to the boy, for wise in the ways of the world, the trader knew that work eased the mind.

Rhythm of the steady pulls dulled Paulo's pain. A friendly wind whispered in the matting that served as sail. Like a live thing the canoe covered the long stretch of open sea, its sharp bow parting the chop into flying spray.

At length they sighted the island of Oahu, the trader's next port of call. Paulo rested his paddle and watched as the high volcanic peak at the island's southern tip grew larger.

"That is Leahy, the place of fire," Boki told him.

"The home of the fire goddess, Pele."

Paulo looked from the curling ribbon of beach to the sharpened peak. The cliff's sheer height above the sea impressed him.

"Some find bright rocks on its slopes," the trader added. "They say these are Pele's tears." As the boy made no comment, the man called loudly: "Perhaps one day you'll find one."

"Perhaps," Paulo agreed, politely.

They went on with their monotonous paddling. Paulo wondered what was beyond the cliff. A large village, maybe?

"Here we must find those willing to care for a homeless boy," Boki said, as though reading thoughts through the back of Paulo's head.

The outrigger canoe plowed through the white spume of breaking waves as they entered the vast, circular bay that fronted Kou. Paulo saw bobbing canoes of all sizes and shapes lined along the beach. Here and there rude pieces of logs thrust blunt noses into the foam. The trader's squinting eyes searched for a landing where he could tie the outrigger for unloading.

Soon, Paulo was standing on the strange and forbiddingly large island called Oahu, feeling as the tiny ant must feel at first sight of a mountain.

The crowded beach, stretching ahead as far as his eyes could follow, frightened the boy. Never before had he seen so many people gathered in one place.

It was a strange and disturbing sight.

He watched as Boki made fast the coconut fiber rope which led in snake-like coils to a stone anchor visible in the clear water below. Then his glance strayed to the heavily-laden outrigger canoe at the end of the rope.

Boki's canoe was a stout one, Paulo thought with relief, since it had made possible their escape across the long expanse of open sea. Now, when the load of sennit cord balls and gourds filled with salt were sold, the trader would leave Kou. And the boy would be left in this strange place to get along the best he could.

Paulo knew this must happen. He did not have to
be told that a small boy would be a nuisance to a
man who had to make his living as a trader.

A great loneliness crept over Paulo. Never had
he stayed with strangers, but now he must.

The lap-lap of water against the worn logs brought
remembrance of a soft voice. Paulo fingered the
carved shell necklace at his throat. He had worn it
since he was a baby. It had been his mother's. "Don't
ever lose it!" she had often warned him. "It's a talisman to bring you luck!"

Paulo had never quite understood what a talisman
was, but he knew it meant something to be highly
prized. Now this string of shells was the only thing
he had to remind him of his mother—truly, now,
they held a treasure.

His eyes burned. If he closed them maybe all this
would change into a bad dream, he thought.

Boki cleared his throat and brought Paulo back
to the present.

"Strangers are welcome on this island," he said.
"But you must stay for many seasons. Yours will be
a hungry mouth to feed, considering how much you
must grow."

Fighting hard to keep tears from his thick-lashed
eyes, Paulo mumbled, "I will eat small."

Boki laughed. "Oh ho! You'll eat much!" he said.
"But that is as it should be. You must grow strong
and big to earn your keep."

"Yes, Boki," Paulo stammered miserably. "I will eat to become strong. I'll be brave."

Boki's serious eyes bored into his. "But always remember, one does not kill and pillage to prove he is brave! There is true bravéry in gentleness. And obedience."

The trader's eyes looked toward the sea.

"Yours was a good village," he went on. "Its people friendly and happy. Your council of elders was fair at all times." His rough fingers bit into Paulo's shoulder. "You must prove this to others by growing into a strong yet peaceful man. Work hard and do your share."

Paulo looked at his toes. The trader made growing up sound so serious. He felt burdened by responsibility.

"I'll try, Boki," he answered.

Boki seemed to sense his misery. The man's lean face softened as he hugged the boy in a clumsy embrace.

"Always remember, little one," he said with great sincerity, "I am your friend. I'll be your true hoaloha!"

Paulo gasped. Such a declaration was not to be taken lightly!

He had never heard such a promise made to a small boy. Gripping tight the trader's rough hand, he held it for a long moment. Strength poured into Paulo's taut body.

"Kou is a wonderful place," the trader said. "There's much to see. And I have another good friend who'll look after us. He is called Olu, the chantmaker. I'm going to ask him to take you to his village."

Paulo still held the trader's hand. "Can't I stay with you a little longer?" he asked, hopefully.

Boki gently loosed his fingers. "Ho, now!" he said. "That's a fine way to start being brave."

"But I don't know anyone. I've never been in a large village. I'm afraid they won't like me!"

"At least you're honest, little one." Boki paused. "Yes, a small village would be best, and not so strange. The one I have in mind is in the valley called Manoa."

"If I go to Manoa, will I ever see you again?" Paulo asked, doubtfully.

"Every trip I make to this island," Boki assured him. "And that will be often!"

The trader's voice sounded relieved, as though he had just made a passage through rough waters.

"Hurry, Paulo!" he added, quickly. "The sun is dipping toward the sea. There is much to be done. We mustn't keep Olu waiting."

Paulo tightened the four foot strip of woven grass which was his loincloth and tucked in the end at his waist. Then he fell into step at Boki's side.

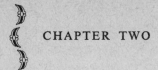

CHAPTER TWO

Paulo Meets the Chantmaker

PAULO had difficulty keeping up with the trader's long strides as Boki led him through one of the worn paths from the waterfront toward the village of Kou.

The boy wondered what Boki's friend would be like, and dreaded meeting the stranger. In all this bustle of activity, he felt small and unimportant. People seemed to be busy everywhere, intent on their own affairs.

The village of ancient Kou, now called Honolulu, was spread over flat grasslands on the protected side of the island. A magnificent crescent of beach formed its western border. At the foot of green, forest-clad mountains a great plain lay like a yellow carpet. A few clumps of tall slender coconut palms and thick green shade trees offered the only retreat from the tropic sun. The peaked roofs of thatched houses scattered in groups over the rolling ground reminded

Paulo of huge stacks of hay, a familiar sight on his home island of Maui.

The houses were made on a frame of lashed wooden poles, and covered with woven leaves or bunches of long, dried pili grass. This formed a thick covering from roof peaks to the ground. A doorway was the only opening. Some had rude fences of closely planted wooden stakes. Others were built on low platforms of black volcanic rocks.

Paulo turned his head this way and that, there was so much to see. People were gathered at the low doorways talking and laughing together. Children and dogs were at play, their cries and barks mingled in a noisy chorus. In the wandering paths and clear-ings that served as streets, boys were flying kites of gaudily painted kapa cloth with bits of feathers dan-gling behind. It was the fall season and the trade winds blew.

Paulo had never seen such magnificent kites!

Under a tall tree near one of the paths, boys and girls took turns swinging from a long, rope-like liana vine. Smaller ones played tag or ran about screaming and turning somersaults. Paulo paid these scant at-tention, but it all looked like great fun, and he would have liked to join in.

Then he remembered that he was a stranger. He peeked to see if the children noticed him walking with a grownup. This made Paulo feel important, in spite of his loneliness.

As they strode past the scattered houses, Paulo saw fat pigs tied with fiber ropes to trees and stakes. These rooted lazily in the dust.

"The chief of this village must be important to have so many pigs," he said to Boki.

Paulo knew that only the chiefs and royal ones could own the pigs, even though the villagers must raise them.

"They have a king on this island," the trader corrected. "He has a palace here in Kou and one on the other side of the mountains. There are also chiefs who act as his advisers." He gave Paulo a pat on the arm. "It's true, there are many pigs. But then this is a rich island."

Fat, waddling ducks and busy chickens moved about pecking for tidbits at random. Noisy birds joined in their chatter; perky island sparrows and gaudily speckled finches which Paulo called by their Hawaiian names.

Boki pointed toward a group of large grass houses set at the edge of a distant clearing.

"There's the palace of the great king!" he explained.

"Which house?" Paulo asked.

"All of them, boy!" the trader assured him. "See the steep roofs? They're built of strong hard ohia timbers. Men took months to cut and carry them all the way from the mountains. And, as you can see from here, only the very longest and finest pili grass is used. They're well-built, indeed. The king lives only on the best on this island!"

"Why so many houses?" Paulo persisted.

"You're truly from a small village, little one," Boki chided. "Have you never seen the palace of a king before?"

"We had a king on Maui, but I never saw him or his palace," the boy admitted, feeling very ignorant.

"Well, there's a house where the king sleeps. One where he eats with his stewards. A house for the women and another where they eat. A cooking house. And of course the temple where the god's images are kept."

Boki waved a careless hand.

"Those smaller ones are for the kauwas, the slaves," he explained.

"Shall we see the king?" Paulo asked, hopefully.

"Ho, now! It's not for us to go looking for the king! It's much smarter to stay out of his way. Anyway, he's on a visit to the big island of Hawaii. I saw him there."

The boy slowed his pace, peering into the distance. If not the king, then sight of one of the great stewards would do.

"Come, laggard!" Boki called, impatiently. "I have much to do."

They turned to the right to enter a large square.

Here, many of the grass houses were finer than any they had passed. One filled an end of the clearing, spreading over at least sixty feet. Boki headed in that direction.

"We go to the men's longhouse," he said. "I must find Olu, my friend."

Paulo's toes kicked little spirals of dust as he padded after the trader.

They made their way between groups of men gathered in the square. Paulo looked at piles of produce at their feet. He watched as men hefted coconuts and poked into the wrappings of bulky bundles. One man inserted a long finger into the mouth of a fat gourd. Slung in a net, the golden bottle was hanging from a carrying pole. The man licked his finger, then smiled with satisfaction.

"I take that one!" Paulo heard him say.

"This must be a market place," the boy told himself, amazed at the variety and abundance of all he saw.

Freshly caught fish lay gleaming in a rainbow of sunlit colors on fresh green banana leaves. Beside them, leaf-wrapped bundles of dried fish, octopi, squid, and rare shellfish were offered for trade. Paulo's nose twitched from their strong sea odors. Piles of yellow and green bananas in various stages of ripeness, smooth-skinned and peach-like mango fruit, and hard kukuinuts with wrinkled shells like old men's faces were laid in neat rows.

Paulo fingered rolls of beaten kapa cloth, in passing. Their soft fibrous sand color was sharply contrasted by intricate designs printed in brilliant colors or sombre browns and blacks. He would like a fine piece of kapa to cover himself at night, he thought, longingly.

Paulo and Boki stepped aside as men stretched out large strips of matting to inspect the weave. This was lauhala matting like that Boki used for the sail on his outrigger canoe. Woven from tough pandanas tree leaves, it had been familiar to Paulo in his own village where he had a length of it for a sleeping pallet.

However, much that Paulo saw was unfamiliar. In his own small village there had been no regular market place. Little was there to trade. After paying tax levies, nothing was left but the bare essentials for living. The chiefs, constantly at war among themselves and other islands, must feed their warriors and also gather tribute for the king.

Near the longhouse now, Boki headed for a group of men who were talking near the open doorway. Paulo wondered which of them would be the trader's friend.

"Aloha oe . . . Olu!" the trader called as he slowed their pace.

One of the men looked towards them. Then he left the group to call:

"Aloha oe! Is it Boki that I see?" He stepped up to the trader and they rubbed noses in greeting.

"Welcome, friend," Olu said. "What brings you here?"

Boki embraced his friend. "Trading, as usual!"

Paulo stood bashfully to one side. When he got the chance to look at Boki's friend, the boy's eyes grew large with amazement. This man was huge! Olu's muscles almost seemed to burst from arms and legs. His massive chest rippled with motion as he walked. A thickly corded neck held high a head topped by an impressive mane of almost curly hair. Boki had called him a chantmaker, but he did not look like a chantmaker, not what Paulo had expected. The great mane of hair, the color of the brown kukuinut, streamed in the breeze. The man's lively eyes were like two glowing coals.

"He is a giant!" Paulo thought with alarm, feeling like a very small frog on a lily pad as he stood looking up at Olu.

The man glanced down at the boy, a good-natured smile curling the corners of his lips. He seemed to be amused by the open-mouthed scrutiny of the small boy. "He looks friendly," Paulo thought with relief.

Boki talked very rapidly to his friend, seemingly forgetting the boy's presence. He told Olu how the warriors had destroyed the little village on the distant isle, all that he had seen, and what Paulo had told him. The boy had never seen the trader so bitter, nor heard him so angry. While Olu listened, the big man's face grew stern.

"The whole village gone?" he asked in a deep rumble that seemed to come from the ground beneath his feet.

Despite his hugeness, the man inspired confidence. Paulo felt sure this man must be as brave as he was strong. He wished this one had been in the village to face the wicked warriors!

Boki pointed toward Paulo.

"This keiki is the only one left alive," he answered, sadly. "He is called Paulo."

Olu frowned, his stern glance making the boy flinch.

"His village must have been poor indeed," the big man said as he looked at Paulo.

The boy's cheeks flamed while he fingered the crude, grass-woven loincloth about his middle. Already, he had noticed that men here in Kou all wore soft kapa cloth and he felt poor and ashamed of his appearance. How could he make a good impression on Boki's friend?

In one startling movement, Olu reached two powerful hands to Paulo's shoulders. He pushed back the boy to see him better in the waning light. Paulo's arms and legs suddenly felt like reeds bending in the wind, he was so embarrassed.

"He needs fattening, this one!" the huge man shouted at large. "Much poi and fat pig will soon fix

him!" Then Olu patted the boy on the back with a
surprisingly gentle touch. "Aloha oe, Paulo!" he said
with a sudden warm smile.

To the boy, this smile was like a flash of sunlight
streaming from between dark clouds. He forgot his
momentary resentment as a feeling of warmth filled
his heart. He raised his hand to touch Olu's arm and
was content as he felt the big man's fingers close
gently in a protective grip. Paulo sensed that he had
made a new friend.

The chantmaker's eyes told the boy not to be
afraid.

Boki motioned, and they all sat on the ground by
the entrance of the longhouse. As the gathering quiet
of early evening stole across the plain, the trader and
Olu talked a long time. Paulo listened to hear if his
name was mentioned. Doubts were beginning to fill
his mind. When would Boki ask the man to take him
to his valley?

He wondered if all the people in Manoa were as
large as was Olu. One would have to eat a great deal
to become as big as that! Thoughts of food made
Paulo's nose twitch. It had been a long time since he
had eaten a proper meal. He became acutely aware
of food odors carried by the breeze.

As he looked all about the clearing, Paulo could
see fires glowing, and thick spirals of steam rising
from freshly opened imus or cooking pits. It was time
for the evening meal. Chatter of voices and quick

laughter brought a lump into Paulo's throat. Almost, he expected to hear his mother's insistent call to supper! It was a difficult thing to be hungry and belong to no one's imu, the boy felt.

At length, Boki rose stiffly to his feet.

"It's settled then?" he asked. "You'll take the boy?"

"Not to my house!" Olu's deep voice rumbled. "Already there are too many mouths."

Aroused now, Paulo listened while his heart pumped in loud thumps. It was being decided!

Olu went on to explain: "I'll have the chief and the Kahuna decide where he's to live."

Paulo knew the Kahuna was the holy man of the village.

Olu added, "Some family must have need of a man child."

"Good!" Boki agreed with a quick nod. "At least you will take him to Manoa. He must go there, being used to a small village and its ways. Paulo will be no trouble."

"I'll take him," Olu answered.

"You're a true friend!" Boki said, thankfully. "I never did have a boy of my own. I almost wish— but, no!" He frowned a protest. "The boy would be a burden to me," he said as though arguing with himself. "Not that he isn't a good keiki and willing to learn," the trader hastened to add. "It's just that—"

"Enough!" Olu said, gently. "It is done! True, a

lone man cannot raise a boy. Even one so fine as this keiki here."

The chantmaker turned to Paulo, a look of compassion softening his features.

"See, the little one is weary. He sleeps!"

Paulo opened his eyes. "No!" he hastened to say.

"You're hungry, then!" Olu observed, knowingly. "Your belly is empty!"

As Paulo scrambled willingly to his feet, Olu pointed.

"We go to the men's lodge and have supper," he said. He chuckled as he playfully ruffled Paulo's hair. "They have a very large cooking oven!"

Paulo grinned in answer. "Now at last I know I am to go with this man," he thought. And he felt that the chantmaker, too, would be his friend.

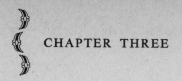

CHAPTER THREE

Boki Says Goodbye

AFTER a restless night spent on strange mats in the men's longhouse and an early breakfast, Paulo watched the golden sun as it rose above the green crest of mountains. Shadows receded like reluctant fingers and the plain of Kou was bathed in sunshine. Olu the chantmaker stood tall by the boy's side in the open square, waiting for the trader to return from his canoe.

"The valley called Manoa is just below the sun," Olu said.

"High up?" Paulo asked.

Olu shook his head. "High up is all rain forest," he explained.

Morning light showed the chantmaker's eyes were as black as night. This surprised Paulo since he had thought them dark brown like the man's huge mane of hair. And in the clear morning air the man looked even taller, with a bulkiness that was almost menacing.

"Where, then, is the village?" Paulo asked.

"At the edge of the yellow foothills." Olu pointed. "Straight ahead."

Paulo looked intently against the sun's glare. "I see nothing," he said.

"All the houses are in a deep valley," Olu explained.

If his own village had been hidden in a valley, Paulo thought, the strange warriors might not have found it. His mother and all his friends might not have been killed so easily. Paulo decided a hidden valley was a good place to have a village.

"Is that where the chief lives?" he asked. "And the Kahuna?"

Paulo had never had words with a holy man nor a chief. Olu had said he was going to take the boy to see them both. They would decide whether Paulo could stay in Manoa. "Is the chief a good man?" he added.

"Morning has filled you with questions!" Olu protested with a deep laugh. "Yes. The chief is a good man. He's called Kuokoa. Some claim he is strict."

The boy knew that the name Kuokoa meant one who stands apart. He wondered if the man was even larger than Olu. The thought troubled him. This chief might not take kindly to a homeless stranger.

"Does Kuokoa have a boy?" he asked.

"Three keikis, he has," Olu answered. "All girls!"

His voice lowered. "Kuokoa lost his only son. About your age he would be."

"What happened?"

"Shark!"

Olu's voice saddened. "The boy was dragged from the chief's great canoe," he said. "During the kona season it was. The water was rough, the winds tricky. About a year ago, it happened. Small fish were scarce. The shark was hungry."

Paulo shivered at thought of the dreaded shark and loss of the boy.

"The shark killed him, then?" he asked.

Olu nodded. His deep-set eyes were turned toward the mountains. "The chief has been difficult ever since," he said, slowly. "Few can get along with him. I think he grieves for his son."

Paulo felt sorry for the chief. He, too, knew loss.

"I wonder . . ." Olu said, aloud. Then he shook his head as though deciding not to speak his thoughts.

Now Boki came striding across the square. Paulo noticed that he carried a small package wrapped in kapa cloth. There was something familiar about the parcel.

"All is well with the canoe!" the trader called.

"We waited to say aloha," Olu said as Boki stopped near them to regain his breath.

"I hurried," the trader gasped. "But I had to

make certain of the anchor." Boki extended his kapa cloth package toward Paulo. "Here, my little friend," he said as his breath returned. "Something for you!"

Paulo could see that the wrapping was scorched and looked familiar.

"For me?" he asked in surprise.

"I found it before we left your village," Boki explained. "It is valuable. You must have it." He laid a hand on the boy's shoulder. "I don't want you to forget me, or your village," he said.

Paulo took the package and started to untie the fastenings. Boki watched, pleasure brightening his long face.

"I will never forget you, Boki," the boy said. His large brown eyes thanked the trader while his eager fingers fumbled with the cord.

When finally the contents was exposed to view, Paulo was at a loss. He did not know what he held!

While leaning forward to see, the .chantmaker's voice boomed with pleasure:

"Aia! It's a splendid pikoi!" he exclaimed.

Boki nodded in answer, his white teeth showing in a happy grin. "One of the best!" he agreed. "From the big island!"

"None make better," Olu said with conviction.

Both men waited for the boy to speak.

Paulo was embarrassed, he did not know what to say.

"I . . . I don't know what it is," he admitted.

Boki laid a finger beside his nose, slyly. "Oh ho! I forget you're not a man of the world!" he chuckled. "Just an ignorant small village boy!"

From the trader's voice, Paulo could tell he was only teasing. But he felt even more uncomfortable.

Boki pointed at the package. "It's a proper pikoi, little one. A throwing stone!" he explained.

"A throwing stone?" Paulo echoed.

He inspected the object in his hands, carefully.

It was not very big, certainly. The handle was short and made of glistening dark wood. The boy saw that it was beautifully polished and carved with small figures. From the end of the handle, a long cord unwound in coils at his feet. He was astonished to see the cord's fineness and close braid. Then he realized it was woven of human hair! At the opposite end, a polished stone knob was fastened so cleverly he could not detect how the work was done.

Boki laid a finger on the pikoi. "The head is of pahoehoe—smoothest lava rock from the volcano," he pointed out with pride. "From high up the slopes of Mauna Kea, it comes!"

Paulo was almost speechless, knowing this was a real treasure. But still, he was puzzled. "What is its use?" he asked, sheepishly.

Boki turned toward the chantmaker.

"You see what an honest boy he is?" the trader

asked Olu. "This one does not pretend!"

"Not many have seen such a weapon, little one," Olu told Paulo. "I know of only one such pikoi in our village. And that is kept kapu! None may touch it. The Kahuna keeps it in the temple with the god images."

This made Paulo feel better.

"Indeed, it is a weapon!" Boki said. "One throws it at whatever he wishes to snare. Either man or beast."

In his eagerness, he took the pikoi from Paulo's hand to flourish it high in the air.

"See the long cord? Well thrown, this wraps about the legs. The quarry trips and falls. You rush in for capture!" He went through the motions of throwing and grabbing. "A skilled thrower can snare large birds with this weapon!" he added as he handed the pikoi back.

Now Paulo realized what a rare thing was the trader's parting gift. "It's a splendid throwing stone!" he exclaimed.

"You'll have to practice long hours to learn its use," Boki cautioned. "It's very tricky."

"I will, Boki!" the boy promised.

Olu's great hand caressed the black, polished

head as it lay in Paulo's hand. "I teach him!" the big man said. "I've seen one used." From the tone of the chantmaker's voice, Paulo knew he wished the pikoi were his own.

"Good, then," Boki said. "You won't forget your village. You won't forget me."

"Even without the gift, I wouldn't forget you!" Paulo answered.

"Well . . ."

The two men and the small boy stood in awkward silence. They did not wish to part.

But each knew it was a long trail to Manoa. Olu must get back to the village and Boki had his goods to trade.

Olu broke the silence.

"Aia! The sun rides high," he said. "Aloha, good friend!"

"Aloha then," said Boki. His voice was gruff.

For a long way up the trail, Paulo kept turning his head to see Boki standing in the large square. The trader never moved as long as they were in sight.

In the open plain, the only sounds were the swish of yellow grass rumpled by the trade wind, morning calls of birds on the wing, and soft pad-pad of bare feet on hard-packed soil. With heart heavy in his chest, Paulo faced the green mountains. He hugged close his new throwing stone.

CHAPTER FOUR

Open Country

PAULO tried to feel happy about going to the valley called Manoa. By the side of the trail he could see broad ponds. Across the ponds were planted long rows of taro root plants. Their broad, heart-shaped leaves glistened in the sun. Rough, volcanic stone ditches led to these ponds from the distant mountains. At first, they puzzled Paulo. Then, he realized the ditches brought water.

"Some say the Menehunes or brown dwarfs built them long ago," Olu explained.

It seemed strange that little men could carry such large stones, Paulo thought. But he knew the Menehunes could work strong magic. Since he was a baby he had been told stories of their marvelous feats.

"They must have worked very hard," he said.

During the course of their walk, grass houses became fewer, smaller, and farther apart. This was truly open country. In the distance behind, they heard the wail of a conch shell trumpet. A mother calling her keikis, the boy imagined. The sound hung in the air, to form the last link with the village of Kou. Now, the plain was all around them.

Olu stopped suddenly, to tug at Paulo's arm.

"Look!" his deep voice whispered.

Paulo looked where Olu pointed. He saw a small bird perched jauntily atop a nettle bush. There was awe in Olu's voice when he said:

"It's the O-o bird!"

Paulo hardly dared to breathe. The boy had never before seen the fabulous O-o bird.

They both watched as the black bird's long curved bill picked insects from the branches. While it jumped about, pale yellow feathers dangled like scraggly patches over each wing. More yellow feathers could be seen tucked under the bird's long tail. Its eyes were glowing yellow circles. With each motion, the lively creature flashed in the sunlight.

"That's the king's color," Paulo whispered, proud of his knowledge.

"Aia! What a rare one!" Olu breathed. "You're right, little one. Only the royal ones may wear these yellow feathers in their helmets and cloaks."

"I have never seen a feather cloak," Paulo admitted.

"Then you've missed a wondrous sight. I can tell you!" Olu said.

"Tell me about it!"

"First, a strong fine net is woven in cord, to the size of the cloak or shape of a helmet."

"How big?"

"The cloak? Either long, to come below the knees, or short to cover just the shoulders. Small bunches of feathers are tied together and fastened to the net in a pattern. Red, yellow, green, black feathers may all be used according to the design which has come to us from very ancient times. Sight of all those feathers together can take your breath away!"

"I would like to have such a cloak!" Paulo said, daringly.

"You dream, boy! It's death to any man who kills the O-o bird. How could you ever have such a cloak?"

"Then how does the king get the feathers?" Paulo asked.

"Birds are snared!" Olu explained. "By official feather gatherers. After the yellow feathers are plucked, the O-o bird is freed to grow more."

"The bird must be angry . . . to lose such pretty feathers," Paulo said with a laugh.

"Perhaps. Anyway, they're hard to find."

They stood and watched until with a shrill call the O-o took flight and was gone.

Now as their steps fell together on the hard trail,

Olu started a chant. His voice was deep and powerful:

> "In the green fields,
>   The god Lono
>   Grows many things.
>   In the bright sky above
>   Birds fly, gracefully.
>   The round sun is warm
>   We are happy
>   We have seen the O-o bird.
>   None may harm it.
>   It flies free

To grow
Soft gold
For adornment
Of our King.
The gods protect it!"

The chantmaker sang this through several times.
Paulo felt lucky to be traveling with a man who
could compose a chant as he walked. "Olu must be
important in his village," the boy told himself.

Soon they passed a pond with a weathered stake
fence around its border. There were no taro plants

here, just open water. Olu's thick lips parted in a grin as he glanced at Paulo.

"Fish pond, my curious one," he said. "It belongs to the king. Kapu!"

As if to prove their presence, leaping fishes skippered across the water's mirror-like surface. They were escaping from a longlegged water bird. The bird's long bill pointed as sharp eyes watched the jumping fish. Then, with one swift dig, its bill was full of wriggling bodies. Long neck jerked from side to side as the bird gulped its catch.

Olu and Paulo both laughed.

"He has no fear of the royal ones," the boy said.

"Aia! He is ignorant, that one!" Olu agreed. "Kapus are not for such things as birds."

The sun rode higher.

Tall coconut palms and wide-spread shade trees etched themselves against the brassy sky. In turn, Paulo and Olu passed beds of sweet potato plants set in hills; more taro patches; clumps of whiskery sugar cane; sprawling gourd vines growing bulging bottles. Even the lowly nettle bush, olona, was growing here in orderly fashion.

Paulo knew that good white cord was twisted from the olona fibers. Only, this was the first time he had seen this bush grown away from the rain forest where it was normally found. He marvelled at the ways of these people on Oahu.

After a time, Paulo was glad to hear Olu call a

halt. This rolling country cut off the force of the trade wind and the many ponds made the air humid. Hot sun overhead baked their skin and they perspired freely. Both were attracted by the deep shade of a thick-foliaged mango tree.

"We rest a while!" Olu said.

Before seating himself on the cool ground, the chantmaker reached a muscular arm high into the waxy green leaves. In two tugs, they each had a ripe, round orange-like mango fruit to eat. While Paulo sucked the sweet juice and chewed the orange-yellow flesh, he thought:

"Surely none go hungry on this island!"

While they rested in the cool shade, Paulo felt like talking.

"You think they will like me in Manoa?" he asked.

Olu wiped his lips with the back of his hand. His eyes twinkled. "Aia, I'm afraid you eat too much," he said. "Three mangos already! And now I must reach for another!"

The boy's face grew red. He choked on the last bite.

"I was hungry, and thirsty!" he defended himself.

"So was I, little one—I but tease," Olu confessed. "No shame in a big belly!" He reached for the largest, ripest fruit he could find. "Eat your fill," he said as he handed it Paulo. "The trail gets steeper."

"Tell me about Manoa," Paulo suggested. He

felt to see if his new throwing stone was secure in his loincloth, and waited.

"Well . . ." Olu began. "Manoa is not very large. But clean and secure. Many trees give good shade. The air is sweet with flowers. Aia, it's a happy village."

Paulo was glad to hear this.

"Are the houses like those in Kou?" he asked.

"Smaller, perhaps. But well built. Many are on rocks and have long tunnels for storing things."

"We had caves," Paulo agreed. "I'd like to see your tunnels."

"So you shall," Olu promised. "There's much to see."

The boy leaned over to wipe his sticky hands on some leaves. Then he scratched his leg where a nettle had stung.

"Will they like a new boy?" he asked the big man.

Olu smiled. "All are friendly," he assured him.

Paulo thought a while. "Will the strict one like me, do you think?" he asked.

Olu averted his eyes. "Kuokoa has few likes these days."

"And the Kahuna?"

"He will do as the chief Kuokoa directs."

Paulo gazed dubiously toward the mountains. "What will happen if they don't like me?" he thought.

CHAPTER FIVE

The Valley Called Manoa

AFTER what seemed to Paulo an endless distance, the trail left the plain and rose steeply. Clumps of thick trees, tropical vines and crowded bushes studded the rocky slopes. The mountain's top was hidden in a thick blanket of grey clouds. Light mist fell in silver streamers through the scattered sunlight.

"Watch your step!" Olu cautioned.

"Are we there?" Paulo gasped.

"Around the bend is the valley."

Paulo tightened his loincloth, fondly patting the hard throwing stone into place. Then he looked back toward the sea. Yellow plain met the deep blue of ocean in a great arc. In the distance, foamy breakers rolled their white froth up the sandy beach. Grass houses of the village of Kou formed tiny brown dots like scattered stones in the dry grassland.

To his right, as far as he could see, steep mountains rose and were lost in great cloud banks and high blue sky. To the south was Leahy where the fire goddess Pele lived.

Paulo leaned against the gritty surface of a hard volcanic rock, his toes curled into the cool wet moss of the trail. He was thinking . . . so much had happened . . . so quickly.

"Come, boy!" Olu called. Paulo could tell the

chantmaker was anxious to be home.

Around the bend the trail turned downward, abruptly leading into tight turns among the rocks. Paulo and Olu had to slide down the loose rubble. And now trees and brush thinned enough for Paulo to catch sight of the valley called Manoa. It lay on the flat of a deep pocket between a cut in the mountain. Surrounded on three sides by tree and vine-clad rocky slopes, the valley's open side faced the blue ocean.

Grass houses were nestled in small clearings in the level places. Some were almost hidden beneath huge flowering trees. Others perched on rocky ledges with their backs to the mountains. Paulo could breathe the scent of flowers in the warm air, just as Olu had told him. This was indeed a pleasing village.

Voices drifted up the slopes and Paulo could see people busy everywhere. A broad, open square formed the village center. The long meeting house was like the one in Kou, only not quite so big. Beside it was a separate clearing. Here stood a group of neat grass houses with a closely staked fence all around. One of these houses had a lanai, or long porch, across its front. These roofs were steeper and higher, and all the buildings were built on a foundation of carefully laid volcanic rock.

"The chief Kuokoa must live there," Paulo decided.

Above this enclosure, closer to the shoulder of

the mountain, was a level place off to itself. Carved wooden images of huge size loomed high on posts in front of a low grass hut.

"That is the temple," Paulo concluded.

He tried to see into the surrounding deep shade for a sight of the Kahuna's house which must be nearby. But he saw nothing that looked like it might belong to the holy man.

Olu urged the boy on.

"A short way and we are there!" he said.

After turning to give Paulo a reassuring grin, the big man's strides lengthened until the boy had to scramble down the trail. Unfamiliar rocks creased his feet. Now Paulo was too busy avoiding stone bruises to worry about meeting the strangers below.

Suddenly, Olu began another chant. His deep voice rang clear in the mountain air as Paulo listened:

> "Hear me . . . you old timers!
>   I return from the great plain.
>   I bring a stranger
>   To the valley called Manoa.
>
>   He is a boy keiki.
>   Wicked men destroyed his homeland.
>   His family is all dead.
>   His village is all pau!
>   It was a terrible pilikia!

The keiki was homeless
And about to starve.
Boki, the trader
Saved the small one.
They sailed across
The many-colored sea
To find our good green land.

The keiki saw the mountains.
They rose from the sea.
He crossed the broad plain.
Now, he sees our village.
He would stay with us!

Bid him welcome
The keiki at your doorway.
And as for me
I am Olu
The maker of chants!

Hunger runs strong
In my empty belly.
My mouth tastes poi.
And steaming roast pig
Carried on the wind.

Who then will make
The big welcome
And call
Aloha nui?"

All the way down the trail, the big man chanted. It was a thrilling thing to hear. But Paulo was embarrassed to be the subject of the chant. So interested in the words was he that it was a surprise when he found himself on the level square.

People gathered. Cries of: "It's Olu! The chantmaker returns!" filled the air. Paulo was proud to be at Olu's side.

"What's the keiki's name?" someone asked.

"Paulo!" Olu thundered in his deep voice.

Soft hands stroked the boy's shoulders. Many children stood about with fingers in mouths and eyes popping. People made way for the large man and the small boy.

"Aloha oe, Paulo!" The boy was greeted in welcome from all sides.

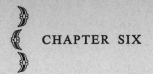

CHAPTER SIX

Crowded House

NEAR the edge of the village square, Olu stopped before a neatly thatched house built among the trees. Children were peeking from behind the cloth hanging that covered its low doorway.

"This is my home," Olu told Paulo.

The boy thought it small for as large a family as the chantmaker seemed to have.

"Anuhea!" Olu called, loudly.

A high-pitched feminine voice answered: "Olu . . . my dear husband!"

"My wife . . ." Olu explained with pride in his voice.

Paulo searched the shadows for sight of one who bore such a pretty name. He knew it meant cool and fragrant. Six small children burst from the house with shouts of welcome. A seventh, very tiny, crawled to the edge of a patch of sunlight at Olu's feet. The big man scooped up the baby in one arm. Then fondly, he rubbed noses with each keiki in turn.

"There are truly many mouths to feed," Paulo
thought as he remembered Olu's words to the trader.
He glanced again at the house. "It's true . . . I can't
live with Olu," he told himself. And in the midst of

this large family, the boy felt more keenly alone than
before.

Paulo was close enough now to see Olu's wife,
seated solidly on a flat rock. A wide strip of kapa

cloth was wound about her middle, binding tight her ample figure. The dress reached to below her very fat knees. Many strands of shell bracelets were wound around her arms. Heavier strands of shark's teeth adorned her ankles. According to ancient Hawaiian standards, Paulo knew that Anuhea was a very beautiful woman.

She greeted the chantmaker with a broad smile.

"You bring new kapa cloth for my middle?" she asked as the big man leaned forward and rubbed noses.

"No piece large enough, my little flower," Olu answered with a deep chuckle.

"Aue! True . . . true!" she admitted with a broad grin. "But . . . I still like presents."

Olu turned to point toward Paulo. "Look," he said. "I have brought a small stranger to Manoa!"

Paulo could feel Anuhea's moist, gentle eyes appraising him.

"Who is this . . . then?" she asked.

Olu told the boy's story.

The keikis all gathered close to hear. Their lively eyes grew large and their mouths opened as the story unfolded. Anuhea clucked with sympathy, quick tears appearing in her soft brown eyes. Paulo was embarrassed at so much attention.

"A great pity," Anuhea agreed as Olu finished. "What is the keiki to do? He cannot live with us. Our house is too crowded."

Anuhea shifted her great weight to lean forward. It was as though she was warming to a time-worn argument.

"We must have another house . . . a men's house!" she said. "You go to the chief Kuokoa and ask to have it built."

Olu protested: "You know I have done so, many times," he said, uncomfortably. "Always, the Kahuna interferes. He says omens are not right for a house-raising!"

Anuhea sniffed. "Aia! He's jealous of your chanting, that one!"

"Perhaps. But we must have his consent."

Anuhea's cheeks turned pink. "Then make a king's chant!" she answered, angrily. "The chief will have to insist your house be built . . . Kahuna or no Kahuna!"

"Men's business!" Olu said, severely.

"And are you not a man?" Anuhea fumed. "Your family must burst through the doorway before you act?" She pointed a pudgy finger toward Paulo. "Must you turn a guest from your house?"

Paulo was very uncomfortable during this argument. Olu seemed to understand how he felt.

"I'll take care of the keiki," he said. "Until Kuokoa decides what is to be done with him."

"Yes . . . in that smelly men's lodge where you also must sleep!"

Anuhea resumed her argument.

"Is a maker of chants," she went on, "to live like a common slave?"

"Let be!" Olu said, losing patience.

Secretly, Paulo felt in agreement with this woman. It seemed a great injustice that a maker of such good chants should have to crowd his family into one small house. The Kahuna must have a powerful hatred to stand in the way, he thought.

Anuhea was not yet finished.

"Better it is that our neighbors care for the keiki," she went on. "A burden he will be to us—we who have nothing!"

"Not so!" Olu protested. "Plenty for all here."

Anuhea looked at the boy with displeasure.

"His loincloth is rudely woven of grass," she persisted. "The keiki has no belongings, it seems, since you both come empty handed."

Paulo fingered the splendid throwing stone tucked at his waist. This woman would not consider such a thing important, he realized.

"Be quiet, woman!" Olu roared. "You embarrass the keiki! And do not speak of the neighbors. I have other plans."

Paulo wondered what plans he meant.

"What would you do?" Anuhea asked, quickly.

"I must think," Olu said, loftily.

"Always you think!" she answered. "Fruit ripens and falls while you think!"

Her ample frame shook as she turned toward

Paulo. A singularly beautiful smile replaced the pout as her round face cleared.

"We touch a sore point, little one," she explained. "Rude we are. You are welcome here!"

"Thank you," Paulo mumbled.

Anuhea turned toward the boy keiki at her elbow.

"Run, Epo!" she said. "Fetch the new bed mat from the house. It's rolled in the corner. And a clean, printed loincloth. Paulo must go to the men's lodge with his own things. None from this house sleep on worn mats!"

Olu's wife is kind, Paulo thought. Her heart is warm despite her sharp tongue! Perhaps the chant-maker *needs* prodding, he told himself with secret amusement.

Olu took advantage of the interruption. "I'll take Paulo with me now," he said. "We're both tired and hungry." He glanced over his shoulder. "I see the men's cooking oven has been opened. Hot food is ready."

"Go, then," Anuhea answered, good-naturedly. "See that the keiki fills his stomach. Small and tight it is!"

"Aia!" Olu agreed. "But he eats big, that one! Aloha, then. Tomorrow we see the chief."

Paulo took the rolled mat and clean loincloth from Olu's son. "Aloha, Anuhea," he said. "Thank you, Epo!"

He hurried to catch up with Olu.

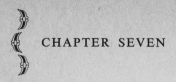

CHAPTER SEVEN

The Kahuna Asks Some Questions

NEXT morning, Paulo awoke to the sound of drums. A constant throbbing beat filled the air. The boy rolled on his new sleeping mat to face the big man sleeping nearby.

"Olu!" he called. "Olu . . . wake up!"

The chantmaker yawned, then tore strong fingers through his great mane of hair. "What is?" he grunted. Half opened eyes turned on the boy, severely. "You destroy my sleep," he protested.

"Drums!" Paulo whispered, urgently. Alarm made his voice rise: "Hear them beat! Is it war?" he asked.

Olu threw off his covering cloth. "Eh . . . what?" Then he relaxed.

"Aia! I had forgotten. It's a feast day."

Paulo lay back on his mat, his heart pumping. The drums made him think of the attack on his village by the vicious warriors.

Ranged along the floor of the longhouse, other

men and boys were awakening. Their woven bed mats checkered the pebble floor. Brilliant slants of morning sunlight streamed through high openings in the thatched walls, as with grunts and yawns a babble of voices began to fill the room.

Heavy drumbeats continued.

"Is it a great feast?" Paulo asked above the din.

"Small," Olu answered with little interest. "To one of our ancestral gods. There are many."

"In my village we also had feast days," Paulo said, trying to make conversation. "In honor of certain trees, rocks and many other things which were always kapu, since they bore the gods' names."

"Many feast days," Olu agreed. "Come, chatterbox, we wash your face, eat plenty poi, and see the fun!"

He arose and stretched. Paulo was fascinated to see strong muscles ripple and form great knots beneath the man's glowing skin.

Presently he asked if they were to see the chief Kuokoa.

A quick frown creased the big man's forehead. "No, today belongs to the hungry one," he said.

Paulo was puzzled. "I never heard of such a one," he said.

"The shark god," Olu explained. "One year ago the shark god took Kuokoa's son," he said, sadly. "Today the Kahuna makes offerings and potent magic so no other will be taken from this village."

The heavy drumbeats grew louder, and Paulo thought about the lost boy.

"Will Kuokoa be seen?" he asked, again.

"The chief's household will be kapu for the day," Olu told him. "None may see them."

The news was a disappointment to Paulo.

"Another day," Olu answered. "Meanwhile, we'll join in the ceremony. I must give remembrance to the chief's son. Afterwards, there were will be games and feats of strength. You'll enjoy them, I think."

"Do you make a chant?" Paulo asked.

"The Kahuna attends to that," Olu answered, shortly.

"Are you working on a king's chant, then?" Paulo asked.

"Perhaps. We shall see." Olu started to turn away. "Too much talk," he said. "Let us eat."

Later, Paulo went with Olu to join in the ceremony for the chief's lost son. All of the people in the village who could come were gathered in front of the temple. Women and girls were in one group, men and boys in another. It was kapu to mingle. Paulo and Olu stood near the stone platform where the Kahuna spoke.

Flower leis or blossom and aromatic leaf garlands draped the huge carved wooden image that represented the shark god. This stood in front of the temple. Calabash and polished wooden bowls

were filled with food and placed at the feet of the
god. Long prayers, incantations, and strange ritual
were solemnly conducted by the Kahuna.

Paulo studied the priest with some misgivings.
The man did not look very friendly, he thought. His
spare figure was clothed with black printed kapa
cloth in the form of a long robe. A short cape covered with black feathers of the frigate bird protected
his narrow shoulders from the hot sun. His body was
bent as he stood and Paulo thought him very old.
The man's bald head glistened and his long face was
filled with wrinkles.

As he spoke, the Kahuna's voice was harsh and
almost croaked like a tree frog on a still night. The
boy shrank from the man's fierce eyes. "Eyes like
those of manu pueo . . . the owl from thunder mountain!" Paulo imagined.

Now the Kahuna faced the gathering and raised
his bony hands for silence and attention. His cracked
old voice started a spoken mele, a chant.

> "From green depths of the broad reef,
>   The monster shark came, a menace!
>   Men paddled in fear.
>   It was the dreaded
>   God of the open waters,
>   The hungry one.
>   The great canoe grew sluggish
>   In the claws of the deep sea.

A son of the chief Kuokoa
Stood bravely in the great canoe.
A curling wave struck unaware!
The keiki fell overside
Into the cruel jaws
Of the hungry menace.

The sea grew calm,
Red colored its waters.
The chief Kuokoa grieved
For the well-loved keiki
The hungry one had taken.

Spare us, mighty god
With the rending teeth.
Ours is a peaceful village.
We love our keikis,
We love our brave men,
We love our good women.

Spare this village,
O hungry one!
You see
We do you honor.
This day is yours,
Mighty god of the sea!"

The Kahuna's voice rasped to a finish.

"I like your chanting better," Paulo confided to Olu in a whisper.

Olu stood straight and tall, never moving a muscle.

It was hard for Paulo to understand why the Kahuna did not allow Olu to make the chants, he whose voice was so melodious and thrillingly deep. "It's really jealousy, then," the boy thought to himself.

The ritual was over.

It was not until after the ceremony that the Kahuna took notice of the strange boy at Olu's side. The priest came to the front of the stone platform and leaned forward.

"Who is this stranger keiki?" he asked, sternly. "Why have I not seen him before?"

Olu stared at the man coldly. "The keiki came at moon time yesterday," he answered.

"Whence came he?" the Kahuna asked.

Olu explained, while the Kahuna kept nodding his bony head and his stern eyes scanned the boy.

"The keiki is homeless?" the Kahuna asked as Olu finished the story.

Olu replied: "Yes, Great One. None live to claim him."

"Then he must have foster parents!" A sly smile formed a crooked line across the Kahuna's chin. "Your house will hold him, perhaps?" he asked.

Paulo felt the chantmaker stiffen by his side as Olu's stormy eyes turned flinty.

"All know I have no men's house." Olu bit the words, as though wanting to say more.

"Aia, yes!" the Kahuna cackled. "It is a matter that is pending. Something about moon changes, wasn't it?"

"Yes," the big man answered, shortly.

"Meanwhile, then, something must be done about the keiki."

The Kahuna leaned forward until his beady eyes were on a level with Paulo's. "What's your name?" he asked.

The boy felt as though he was turning on a hot spit. "Paulo, Great One," he answered.

"Have you learned to be useful?"

"I don't—you mean?"

The Kahuna's voice grew cold. "Have you a knife of sharp shell, or tortoise?"

"No, Great One."

"I could use another woodcarver," the Kahuna mused. "A stone adze, then?" His lips hung slack. "Sharp and well polished?"

"No."

"Have you learned to beat kapa bark?"

"What does he expect of a boy?" Paulo thought. He began to stutter with fear and discomfort. "We had little—I never—I mean—no," he ended, miserably.

The Kahuna was relentless.

"Can you twist olona fiber to make strong cord? Pound the taro root for poi? Can you braid? In fact," he paused for breath, "can you do anything useful?" he finished, disdainfully.

Olu interrupted. Paulo could see that the chant-maker was very angry. "He's but a keiki, as you can plainly see!" Olu said.

"Let the boy answer for himself," the Kahuna reprimanded, severely. "I but wish to learn his talents, if any!"

The Kahuna straightened his back, stretching his slight frame to its most impressive height. "Can you do anything, then?" he asked.

Paulo was terrified. How could he hope to stay in this lovely village if the Kahuna did not like him? He bit his tongue to force it to speak. He must say something!

"I . . . I can weed . . . taro," Paulo answered.

"A farmer boy!" the Kahuna snorted, making it sound a worm's occupation. "We have plenty of such here," he added. "You must have a skill to stay in this village, stranger that you are."

Olu came to the rescue: "The boy owns a very rare throwing stone," he told the Kahuna.

The priest turned in surprise. A crafty look made slits of his eyes as Olu continued.

"It came from Mauna Kea, the volcano on the big island. Its handle is made of a wondrous hard wood, cleverly designed. Its head is of the smoothest lava. All know there is none better!"

The Kahuna looked at Olu with venom in his glance.

Both men knew that there was only one such throwing stone in Manoa. And the Kahuna had it in his possession, making it kapu to all. Another such valuable weapon would give the young boy considerable prestige in the village.

Olu stared hard at the Kahuna, a secret smile of satisfaction almost curling his full lips. Paulo felt grateful for Olu's help. He knew the interview was going badly—this Kahuna did not want him in the village, he felt sure. He rubbed the hard, polished head of the throwing stone tucked at his waist.

Then a strange thing happened.

It was as though a vision filled the boy's eyes as he rubbed the stone. Boki, his friend, seemed to be standing right beside him. "Courage!" the trader's lips were saying. And remembrance of the kindly smile gave the boy instant comfort. Loneliness and anxiety left him. He no longer felt so afraid of the Kahuna. "My throwing stone is a talisman," Paulo thought with great wonder.

"Can you throw the stone, my young one?" the Kahuna asked, smoothly.

Before Paulo could answer, Olu spoke: "The keiki has had little chance to practice, Great One. It was a parting gift from Boki the trader. But I will teach him. He's quick to learn."

The Kahuna glanced sourly at them both.

"The keiki must become expert!" he said with finality. "Meanwhile I shall ask the great chief, Kuokoa, about the boy. The chief will decide whether there is a home in Manoa for him."

Abruptly the Kahuna turned his back. Paulo knew the questioning was ended, and he wondered what his fate would be.

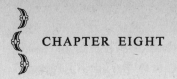

CHAPTER EIGHT

A Short Spear

AS THOUGH relieved that the sad part of the day was finished, the people were now laughing and shouting. The air was filled with excitement.

"Come! We will see the games and the sports!" Olu told Paulo with a sudden smile.

"Will you take part?" the boy asked.

"Perhaps!"

Paulo lifted his head. "You'll win," he said.

"Oh, ho!" Olu chuckled. "I have one who believes in me! But there is a foot race for you to compete in. Hurry, it is about to start."

Indeed, Paulo saw that a group of five boys were standing in a line. A hundred paces off, a man held a flagged pole, waiting to start the race. All the boys were about Paulo's age.

"There'll be a prize!" Olu said, pushing the boy along. "You must win it."

"Can a stranger . . . run?" he asked, dubiously.

"Why not? Come, I'll hold your throwing stone."

Paulo was filled with doubts. However, he wanted very much to please the chantmaker. In his own village, he had run such races. Perhaps he could win.

He allowed the big man to thrust him forward toward the starting line. People noticed and gathered round with good-natured interest.

"Look!" they said. "The stranger will run. It's Paulo!"

Paulo knew he could not back out now.

Olu examined the boy's feet for stone bruises. Finding them in good shape, he patted Paulo on the back.

"Pace the others," he whispered. "Save your strength for the finish."

Paulo had never been told such a thing before. Always, he just gritted his teeth and ran. Seldom had he won a race, it was true. He would try to remember Olu's advice.

The race started from a standing position.

Paulo was placed at the side of the lineup. Next to him, a fat boy stood swinging his arms. Paulo took a quick look at the boy. He was powerfully built, and his legs were long.

None of the contestants looked directly at each other, even when Paulo joined the group. Only side-long glances were exchanged, then eyes turned straight ahead, grimly. Each was determined to win the race. They stood tensely waiting for the signal to be given.

Now that Paulo was about to start, the man with the flag seemed very far away. The boy's heart pumped anxiously. He hoped he would not disgrace himself, and Olu.

The signal was given!

All six boys dug their toes into the dust. Knees lifted. Paulo burst into a fast stride, the fat boy right beside him. Feeling that he could outdistance the fat one, he increased the pace. The fat boy came faster, staying neck and neck. Then, out of the corner of his eye, Paulo saw a taller boy take the lead. All the boys were pressing too hard.

Paulo began to gasp for breath. His feet were hard to steer as, desperately, he tried to increase his speed to overtake the tall boy. The fat one was forgotten for the moment, though he stuck stubbornly at Paulo's side. He felt himself tiring. The fat boy crowded close, causing Paulo to miss a stride. He closed again and Paulo almost stumbled, then managed to clear his feet.

"This one means to win at any cost," he thought, grimly.

Now the fat boy forged ahead with a quick spurt, seemingly wanting to overtake the taller one's lead. He paid no more attention to Paulo.

"He thinks I'm out of the race," Paulo realized swiftly.

Then, he thought of his breathing because his chest hurt and he was concerned, knowing he would do well to even finish the stretch. Olu's deep voice came to him from the crowd:

"Run, Paulo! Run!" the big man was yelling.

Now Paulo remembered Olu's words before the race. He stopped pressing and his stride grew easier.

Doggedly, he thought only of keeping up with the leaders. Strength must be saved for the finish—but a win seemed hopeless, only half the course was run.

The crowd yelled encouragement according to their choice. Few yelled Paulo's name since the fat boy was their favorite. Grimly, Paulo paid more attention to his stride. Breathing became strangely easier. A glance showed the fat boy's face was red and the tall one was slowing his pace.

Three boys were now abreast. The tall one, the fat one, and Paulo.

Without realizing how, Paulo was more easily keeping up with the others. "Olu was right!" he thought, dazedly. "I still have strength."

The man with the flag loomed larger. A few paces ahead was the finish. The crowd's yelling became a roaring jumble in Paulo's ears. He shut his eyes and pumped his feet, running desperately with lungs that were bursting and legs that felt like water-soaked logs. He had never tried so hard before.

Olu's strong arms caught Paulo as the boy stumbled—the race was over! The crowd cheered mightily.

Pounding in Paulo's ears gradually lessened and his chest stopped cramping. He was too spent to ask Olu how he had done, as through clearing eyes he watched the man with the flag approach.

The crowd parted.

The man's free hand held a short spear. Its head

was a double barb of stone, beautifully notched and rubbed smooth. This was the winner's prize. The man held the spear toward Paulo.

"This boy was fastest," he said, handing over the spear.

"You win! You win!" Olu crowed as he hugged Paulo close.

Panting for breath and speechless, Paulo grasped the spear in his shaking hand.

Again, the crowd cheered: "Paulo! Paulo is the winner!"

A broad smile brightened the boy's face as he glanced about in embarrassment. "They call me by name," he thought, gratefully. His round eyes sought Olu's.

"The village . . . has given me . . . a present!" he said, aloud.

"Aia! You did well!" Olu agreed.

The smooth shaft of the new spear felt warm in the boy's grasp.

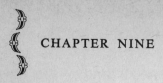

CHAPTER NINE

An Error of Judgment

AFTER the games, Paulo and Olu went to the feast or luau and ate plenty of roast pig and poi. The pig was a gift from the chief Kuokoa to the villagers, in honor of his lost son. There was also plenty of other food—baked sweet potatoes, smoked fish, bananas baked and fresh, as well as many varieties of fruit. Paulo ate until Olu was afraid the boy's small belly would burst.

Gorged with food and refreshed, they found a place under a broad shade tree and rested. Silky fronds of a tall coconut palm nearby reached high to sing happily in the brisk trade wind. Olu covered his face with a long green ti leaf and snored through a short nap. Paulo watched the crowd. Recognizing the boy in passing, many of the villagers greeted him by name. Some complimented him on his running.

It was good to feel he was a part of the activity.

After Olu finished his nap, Paulo ventured a question: "Could we—will you teach me how to throw my stone?" he asked, hopefully.

Olu rubbed his eyes. "Aia! You give me no peace!" he chuckled. "After eating so much, you should sleep for a moon's quarter."

"Please, Olu," the boy begged. "I feel fine!"

"Help me up, then. I've taken root!"

The chantmaker pretended to lean heavily on Paulo's support. They both laughed merrily at the idea of such a small boy lifting a big man.

"Lean your new spear against this trunk," Olu said, pointing to the tree nearby. "It hasn't left your hand since you won it."

Paulo took the throwing stone from his loincloth. The long cord of braided hair unwound to his feet as he grasped the smooth handle, fondly. Paulo wished that his friend Boki were here to see him practice.

Olu chose a small tree nearby as a target. He motioned Paulo to a few paces away.

"Now, hold the head so," he instructed. "Hold the cord in your left hand, and swing it."

Paulo tried to do as Olu directed, but he was clumsy. The chantmaker shrugged his broad shoulders.

"No, with arm extended!" he said. "Aia! Let me show you."

He took the handle and swung it with graceful ease. The stone flew toward the tree and its cord caught on the slender trunk. Rapidly swinging about the tree, the stone head hit the bark with a solid thump.

"You see! If that were a man, he'd be tripped and fall," Olu exclaimed with satisfaction.

Paulo marvelled. For the first time, he truly realized the throwing stone's usefulness.

"It looks easy," he said.

"Perhaps." Olu grinned. "Now you try!"

Paulo practiced this simple throw for a time. Once or twice, he got the cord to wrap about the tree, but never as completely as Olu.

Then the chantmaker found a short log. He tied this with a piece of rope and threw the loose end over a branch of the larger tree where they had been resting. This end he made fast to the trunk.

"You'll not find this so simple," he cautioned as he started the short log swinging back and forth, slowly. "We use a moving target," he explained with a grin.

Paulo eyed it doubtfully. "I must hit that?" he asked.

"Of course! Think you the quarry will wait to be plucked like a ripe gourd?"

Paulo's face grew warm as many times he threw the stone at the swinging log. The target seemed stubborn and contrary, now most elusive. Either the cord tangled around his wrist, or he threw too directly and the head bounced off the log. Only by accident, it seemed, did he manage to wrap the cord about the log's middle.

"It has a will of its own," he said ruefully, wondering if he could ever master such a difficult weapon.

"I'm clumsy!" he said, after a time.

"Aia! That you are, little one," Olu agreed with a great laugh. "I told you it wasn't easy. Skill comes only with practice."

A group of small children and men with nothing better to do stood about calling all kinds of useless advice. Not one had ever seen a throwing stone. But all were quite willing to tell the boy how to use it. This made Paulo feel important and anxious to show improvement. He practiced so long a time, Olu tired of watching.

"This is enough for now," the chantmaker told Paulo. "We leave the log hanging. No one will disturb it."

"Must I stop?" Paulo asked.

"Please yourself. But it seems you've done enough for one day!"

"I'll practice more. Then I'll try my new spear."

"Like a king's warrior you are, with so many weapons!" Olu chuckled. "The spear is dangerous. Be careful! Throw only against a broad tree, well out of the way."

"I'll be careful."

Olu waved a hand. "I'll find you later."

After a time, Paulo tired of throwing the stone. He wandered off to find a good target for his new spear. Leaving the main square, he eyed the trees along its border. Either there were too many people about, or keikis were busy with their games. A tree off by itself was hard to find.

The search brought him close to the stake fence of the chief's courtyard. Because of the kapu, there were no people here. Paulo spotted a large tree with a good broad trunk. It seemed a splendid target. Standing back a short distance, he let go the slender shaft.

Like crisp lightning it flew!

The barbed head found its mark in thick bark. Paulo hurried over to withdraw the spear, being careful not to loosen the head. He had thrown sharpened sticks as darts ever since he was a small keiki. His aim was not too wild. The wide trunk of the tree was an easy target. Paulo had a wonderful time and was delighted with his new prize.

Then he moved back for a long throw. Like a bird in flight, the slim spear arced through the air and missed the tree. It sailed right over the stake enclosure and into the courtyard of the chief.

Paulo was dismayed. The courtyard was kapu, he knew. The royal flag waved in the breeze as a warning. Either he must violate the kapu . . . or lose his newly won prize. He glanced about. Then he placed an eye between the stakes and anxiously peered all around the courtyard. He hoped someone would see the spear and return it. Hope died. No one was in sight, and Paulo dared not call out. He knew he would be severely punished for breaking the kapu but he would have to risk this to get help.

Unhappily, Paulo retraced his steps and sat down in the dust. He knew he should have been more careful . . . looked past the tree. But the damage was done. Loath to leave without his spear, Paulo got back on his feet and trudged to the stakes for another look. "Maybe I can see where it fell," he told himself.

This time he looked toward the chief's house and gasped with alarm!

The spear was in sight, certainly. But its sharp head had pierced the chief's personal water gourd. A big, fat yellow one, sitting within a few paces of the chief's doorway, on the ground near the porch. Even now, water was spilling across the ground in a muddy stream. From where he stood, Paulo could see that the ornately decorated gourd was hopelessly ruined.

The enormity of his crime made his knees tremble. As owner of the spear, he knew he would be identified. He could not leave it. Most of all the disgrace he would bring to Olu! And the loss of his new prize!

As he stood leaning weakly against the hard stakes, there seemed to be only one solution. He must recover the spear. Further along, he could see a break in the line of stakes. This formed a side entrance to the chief's house. With trembling knees, Paulo moved to the corner post and looked in. A

sudden breeze whipped the kapa streamers of the
flag with a loud pop!

Guiltily, Paulo glanced upward. It had sounded
like a warning.

The chief's house was about twenty paces from
the stake fence. To Paulo, the distance seemed more
like an ocean's width. He took a deep breath, deciding that a quick dash might do it! Like the flash flood
of a sudden downpour in the rain forest, the boy ran
across the clearing, grabbed the shaft of the spear
and tugged it loose, turned and started a hasty
retreat.

Without warning, a black cloud seemed to en-
gulf Paulo. His frantic hand tried to tear it aside,
to make good his escape. Then he realized what
his fingers held.

It was the black robe of the Kahuna!

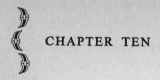

CHAPTER TEN

Paulo Meets the Great Chief

"OOPH!" the Kahuna exploded as Paula sprawled at his feet.

Terrified, the boy stared up at the angry face.

"The stranger keiki!" the priest exclaimed as he recovered breath. He stepped back to straighten his black cape and brushed a scrawny hand across his robe. "What mischief brings you here?" he asked, quickly, eyes burning with resentment. "Know you the chief's courtyard is kapu?"

"I meant no harm!" Paulo gasped.

"You carry a spear!"

"I but lost it, Great One!"

The Kahuna glanced angrily towards the porch. There was the broken gourd. Water muddied the ground—the story was plain to see. Breath exploded from the Kahuna's narrow chest.

"You destroy Kuokoa's property, wretched boy!" he said.

"It was an accident, Great One."

"You dare trespass on forbidden ground?" The Kahuna shook his bony head. "Come!" he ordered and his slight figure stalked toward the chief's house.

Paulo scrambled to his feet. After picking up the offending spear, he fell into step behind the Kahuna. "Now, I am truly lost," he thought with fear and trembling. "The chief will kill me—or send me away. Lock me up! Or even make me a slave!" Paulo wanted to turn and run.

As they approached the porch, a tall man with greying hair appeared at the doorway of the chief's house. He wore a magnificent yellow loincloth which reached to his knees. Around his high forehead was a band of polished shells. A pendant of carved walrus tusk beads hung at his neck. Paulo knew he must be Kuokoa, the chief.

The Kahuna halted Paulo with a rough hand thrust backward.

"On your knees!" he ordered. "Face the dust!"

The boy dropped to the ground and knelt before the chief. With heart thumping and jaw cramping, he tried hard to keep back tears. He wished he had eyes in the top of his head.

"What brings you?" Kuokoa asked the Kahuna, mildly.

"My business can wait, Great One," the Kahuna said with a fawning bow. "I captured this wretched keiki at your gate. A rash one who has destroyed your property!"

"Indeed?" Kuokoa's face was stern. "Destroyed my property, you say?"

The priest pointed a bony finger toward the ruined water gourd: "This daring one chose the royal gourd as a target for his spear," he said. "As you can see, it is shattered and quite useless!"

Paulo turned his head to steal a look at the Kahuna. "He speaks a lie!" he muttered under his breath. But the boy dared not defend himself in the presence of the mighty chief.

Kuokoa took a long look at the gourd, his face unmoving. Then another long look at the stake enclosure twenty paces away. And finally, a careful scrutiny of the small boy kneeling in the dust.

"Where did the keiki stand?" he asked.

"Eh . . . what? Stand?" the Kahuna echoed.

"From where did the keiki loose the spear?"

Flustered by the question, the Kahuna waved his hands. "I caught him, Great One!" he said. "He was running from the courtyard. The spear was in his hand. I acted quickly to catch him." His mouth grimaced with satisfaction. "As you can see, the gourd is broken. I know not where the boy stood," he ended.

The chief's face was sternly set as he looked at Paulo.

"Perhaps we should question the keiki," he suggested. "We must know all details of such a serious crime."

"Yes, yes! He must be made to tell!" the Kahuna hastily agreed.

While he listened, a hard lump formed in Paulo's throat. He did not know how he could possibly speak to the Strict One.

"You may stand, boy," Kuokoa directed.

The chief glanced toward the Kahuna. Some of the severity left his voice as he asked: "Surely this is a remarkably accurate shot for one so young?"

"The gourd is broken!" the Kahuna pointed out.

"Yes, I see. Well . . ."

As Paulo rose to his feet and lifted his head, the chief stopped talking. Their eyes met. Kuokoa gave a short gasp of surprise, his face paling. He looked at the boy, long and searchingly. Wondering what could be the matter, Paulo stood as though hypnotized.

At length, Kuokoa seemed to recover, as from a great shock. His deep voice shook a little when he asked: "You threw the spear . . . from where?"

Paulo motioned with an unsteady hand. Something seemed to be wrong with the chief. But the boy could not fathom what it could be. The gourd must be very valuable, he thought with a sinking heart.

"There, Great One, beyond that tree," he answered.

"The one outside?" Kuokoa asked, doubtfully. "Beyond the stakes?"

"Yes, Great One." The boy's glance fell. "I was practicing."

"Practicing, eh?" A frown darkened the chief's eyes as he turned to the Kahuna. "You told me my property was the boy's chosen target," he said sternly.

"It was! It was, Great One!" the Kahuna assured him.

"From beyond that tree—" the chief raised a slender hand to point, "it would take a skilled hunter to hit the gourd. Only by accident could this keiki have shattered it!"

The Kahuna's face was stony.

A surge of relief flooded Paulo. At least the Strict One was fair, he thought.

"The keiki trespassed!" the Kahuna insisted. "I found him within the courtyard. All know it is kapu!"

"That is true," Kuokoa agreed. "I watched you bring him."

"The gourd is broken!"

"That also is true." The chief looked at Paulo. "What say you, boy?" he asked. "You meant to break the gourd?"

"Oh, no!" Paulo protested. He decided to admit everything. "I threw too hard, and missed the tree. I'm clumsy, Olu says. It was my new spear. I never had one before. Just today I won it."

Kuokoa's eyes lighted with interest. "You won the spear?" he asked.

"Yes, Great One. A present from the village for winning the footrace."

The chief nodded. "You are fleet of foot also, then!" he said, amiably.

Kuokoa seemed pleased that he could run, but Paulo decided it would be better not to answer.

The chief turned to face the Kahuna. "The keiki is a stranger in Manoa," he observed.

"Yes, Great One." The Kahuna hastened to explain. "An outlander from one of the islands to the south," he said, pompously. "A homeless waif. His whole village was destroyed, his people killed."

"How could this be?" the chief asked.

"Renegade warriors, Great One, of which we have heard."

"Devils!" Kuokoa protested. "The king must wipe them out. No island will be safe!"

"True . . . true, Great One!"

"How came the keiki here?"

"Boki, the trader, brought him to Oahu. For some reason, he sent the keiki to Manoa with Olu the chantmaker."

Kuokoa turned toward the boy. "From which island did you come?" he asked, intently.

"Maui, Great One," Paulo answered. "From a very small village near the sea. It had no name."

"I see. From Maui, you say!"

Kuokoa continued to stare at Paulo, seemingly unable to keep his eyes off the boy's face. Sadness and longing was evident in the chief's eyes. Paulo felt most uncomfortable under the scrutiny. At length, the chief's glance seemed to freeze on the necklace at the boy's throat, noting every detail. Unconsciously, Paulo raised a hand to finger it.

"Come closer," Kuokoa whispered suddenly.

Startled, the boy obeyed.

The chief reached a hand to Paulo's throat and lifted the carved shell necklace. He stared at it a long time, turning it this way and that. His face, meanwhile, grew extremely pale.

"Where did you get this?" he asked softly.

"From my mother," Paulo answered. The boy was troubled. Did Kuokoa think it was stolen? "I've worn it since I was a small keiki," he hastened to explain.

The Kahuna crowded close, to see. When the priest straightened his skinny back to look at the chief, there was wonder in his eyes.

"You recognize the symbols?" Kuokoa asked through trembling lips.

The Kahuna nodded. A crafty expression squinted his eyes. He said nothing.

Kuokoa seemed to be overcome with emotion. He let drop the shell strand and gazed toward the sea. When, finally, he spoke, it was as though none were present:

"And Boki the trader brought the keiki to Kou, then sent him on here. What a strange thing! How could it be possible? How can I be sure?"

Paulo was mystified by the interest in his necklace. "I didn't steal it!" he assured the chief. Not knowing why, he felt like crying.

"Hush, boy!" the Kahuna intervened. "No one accuses you of such a thing."

Kuokoa roused himself. "The keiki meant no harm—let him go," he said. "This is not a day to punish small boys. I must think!"

He moved toward the doorway, then hesitated. "Where do you stay in the village?" he asked the boy.

"At the men's longhouse," Paulo answered. "The chantmaker has no room."

"That is strange!" Kuokoa looked at the Kahuna. "I agreed Olu was to have a new men's house. Why has it not been raised?"

A toothy grin distorted the Kahuna's face. "Omens were not right, Great One," he hastened to explain. "We cannot offend the gods!"

"You delay? The chantmaker's family is large. The boy keikis should be in a men's house with their father!"

The Kahuna rubbed his hands. "The moon phase must be right, Great One. I waited to set the most auspicious day. The gods must be pleased. No harm must come to our good chantmaker!"

Paulo recognized sarcasm in the priest's voice. "He will stop at nothing," the boy thought. "Lies seem to suit his purpose."

"You know best, I suppose," Kuokoa agreed, absently. "The gods must be appeased."

Paulo dared to ask a question: "May I stay here in Manoa, Great One? It's a wonderful valley and . . . and I like the people."

Kuokoa smiled wanly. "They will like you, I think," he answered. "But I have not yet decided what to do. You must have guidance. It seems you get into mischief easily." He pointed toward the gourd and shook his head. "You must have a watchful father to care for you."

A sly smile twisted the Kahuna's face. "Who then will take the boy?" he asked.

Kuokoa gave him a long look. "I will think on the matter," he answered, coldly.

"Meanwhile?"

"See that Paulo comes to no harm. Tell the chantmaker he is responsible for the keiki until I decide what is to be done." Kuokoa glanced at Paulo, raising a hand of dismissal. "You have the makings of a great hunter!" he told the boy with a sudden warm smile. "Your legs are strong and your spear has a long flight!"

The Kahuna motioned the boy away. "Come!"

Paulo was glad to leave the chief's presence. It was a relief to have received such fair treatment, he felt. And he was truly sorry to have broken the gourd. He would be more careful in the future.

"The chief is a fine man," he told himself.

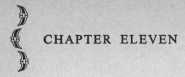

CHAPTER ELEVEN

Chant of the Menehunes

"**M**AYBE you spoil everything!" Olu told Paulo the next morning.

Subdued and worried after a restless night, the boy had described his meeting with the chief.

"I'm sorry," Paulo answered.

He wondered what the chantmaker meant, but he felt he dare not ask.

"You're lucky," Olu added. "Many have been punished for breaking a kapu, little one. Was nothing said about who takes you?"

Paulo hung his head. "Kuokoa didn't say I could stay," he admitted.

"At any rate you have a whole skin!"

The boy remembered something. "The chief asked why I wasn't staying in your house."

"Aia!" Olu frowned. "He knows my house is crowded!" His big fist clenched. "Long have I waited for a new one!"

"The Kahuna talked of moon phases."

"The moon—bah! He purposely delays, that one!"

Paulo agreed. "The chief seemed to think so, but when the Kahuna talked of gods the chief was silenced."

"Nothing was decided? No date set for a house-raising?"

"No."

Olu let the subject drop.

It was early morning. Cooking ovens were beginning to smoke as they were heated for preparation of the day's food.

Today it was Olu's turn to tend the cooking oven of the men's eating house. Already, he and Paulo had gathered food and large bundles of wood for their fire. They both knelt in the blackened dust beside the pit.

"Hand me that old piece of kapa cloth," Olu directed. "I will teach you to make a flame."

Paulo was surprised. "I can fetch another's burning ember," he offered.

"No! You must learn useful things. We start now," Olu said, sternly.

And Paulo settled by his side, willingly enough.

Olu held a soft stick with a groove worn down its center. As his knees gripped the stick, he rubbed back and forth with the point of a hardened twig. His fingers worked rapidly, with skill and power. Soon there was a smoking button of dust at the end of the groove. Olu increased the friction.

The dust ball glowed.

Olu tumbled the spark onto the frayed kapa cloth and fanned it with a leaf. A tiny flame burst with a thin spiral of smoke. This flickered redly, then grew to a smoldering ember.

"Quick! Dry moss and small twigs," he grunted.

Paulo laid a pyramid on the glowing ember while Olu fanned. Soon a crackling fire was started. Glow from its yellow light brightened their freshly scrubbed faces. Soft warmth radiated, cheerily.

"Now you see? That is how to do it," Olu said.

Carefully, he laid the fire in the center pit of the cooking oven which was formed as a hollow place in the ground and lined with basalt rocks. These water-worn volcanic boulders could stand intense heat without cracking or exploding. As the fire increased, its warmth penetrated quickly through the porous rocks. Olu and Paulo fed a constant supply of wood to the blaze until the oven was like a furnace filled with glowing coals.

"Enough," Olu said.

They piled the rocks all over the fire, and after these were thoroughly heated, the fire was allowed to burn down. With sticks, they scraped out the glowing embers and burned wood since these had served their purpose. It would be the hot rocks that did the cooking, not the fire.

Paulo had ready a bundle of fine green grass.

With this, he helped Olu line the hot oven. They both coughed from the smoke and tangy steam.

"Now, the food!" Olu grunted when the bottom was thickly covered with grass.

Hunks of pig flesh wrapped in green ti leaves were placed on the bottom of the oven. These already had been sprinkled with coarse sea salt. Olu and Paulo then took sticks and tumbled hot rocks from the sides of the pit. With a great hissing and popping, the hot rocks settled between the packaged food.

"Here are the banana leaves," Paulo said as he dragged a pile to Olu's side.

They covered the whole jumble of rocks and food with the big, wide leaves to form a thick layer. More hot rocks were pushed onto the pile.

"Plenty sweet potatoes!" Olu ordered.

The long tubers were soon scattered over the surface of the green banana leaves. Already, steaming food odors made their mouths water.

"Banana stalks!" Olu ordered next. "Lively, little one!"

The water-filled, fibrous stalks of the banana tree had been crushed and split and now formed a smothering layer to cover the food and rocks in the pit. Hot slivers of steam spurted between the cracks as wet fibers touched white hot stones. The whole oven was then covered with layers of old mats and kapas to blanket the moisture and heat. A final layer of loose earth finished the job. Not a single spiral of

steam betrayed the oven, which would be left all day
to do its work unattended. Pressure of the hot steam
would cook the food. The meat would be tender and
the vegetables bursting with their juices. This was the
way the Hawaiians had cooked since ancient times.

"Now all shall have plenty," Paulo said with a
laugh. "I can hardly wait to taste the pig!"

"I put in a big piece for your small belly," Olu
chuckled. "For once we may fill it!"

After they gathered the broken twigs and extra
leaves, Olu turned to Paulo.

"What say you to an adventure?" he asked,
casually.

Paulo looked up with quick interest.

"We go to the rain forest!" Olu told him.

"Up the mountain?" Paulo asked.

"Aia! We gather olona bark."

"And I may help?"

"Of course. You must earn your keep!"

Paulo stood up. "I'm ready," he said. Then, as
an afterthought: "May I take my throwing stone?"

"As you wish. And I'll lend you a small adze."
Olu laughed. "You'll be loaded!"

"I am strong," Paulo insisted, enthusiastically.

"The day is just born," Olu cautioned.

Paulo knew that the olona was usually found
growing in moist ravines of the native forests. Since
old enough to toddle, he had seen olona fiber used
for making strong cord. The shrub was plentiful on

his native island of Maui. Here on Oahu, he had seen
it grown in plots on the great plain near Kou. In the
valley of Manoa, the people were closer to the natural supply and did not bother to grow the plant.

Bast fibers from the inner bark are the strongest
natural fibers in the world! The villagers used it for
fishlines and nets, for tying crude bone fish hooks,
and wherever strong small cord was needed. Stripped
from branches about six feet long and rolled into
coils, the olona was carried to the village for soaking
and scraping.

"I go to fetch the adzes and my carrying pole,"
Olu said.

At length they were ready. Olu headed for a deep
ravine near the crest of the mountain. The trail rose
steeply from the valley floor to wind through thickets
of lush-growing brush, moist trunks of trees covered
with thick green moss, past huge rocks almost hidden by tangled liana and morning glory vines. Pushing their way upward through this most unyielding
growth, both were soon winded.

"We rest, eh?" Olu suggested.

Morning air was damp and heavy. Water dripped
from lush green foliage, tinkling like tiny bells as it
splashed from rock to rock. Sodden bass notes came
from soft wet moss and leaf mold, rotting logs, and
nodding broad leaves of aromatic ferns. These
formed an almost solid wall of vegetation to line
the way.

Paulo knew that here was the start of the rain forest, a place bathed daily from intermittent showers spilled from scudding clouds, driven from far out to sea by the strong trade winds.

"What a wonderful place!" Paulo said, softly.

"Aia!" Olu agreed. "But difficult to climb!"

They leaned against the moist black volcanic rocks.

Below, they could see the village as it sprawled across the valley. Rosy morning light brought every detail into sharp relief. Through the clear air, sounds floated with amazing clarity. A dog's querulous bark broke the stillness. This was followed by a raucous chorus throughout the village as other dogs joined in. Women could be seen walking about doing early morning chores. Keikis already were at play. Deep men-voices sounded their authority. Sharp blows of an adze tore against a stubborn log. Hollow thumps from poi boards and stone pounders added a steady beat.

"Look above," Olu waved a hand. "Up there, some say the Menehunes live!"

Paulo peered into the gloom. "The little brown men who built the ditches?" he asked, remembering the legends he had heard.

"The very same!"

"Have any seen them?"

"So it is claimed."

"What did they look like?"

Olu scratched his head.

"No story is quite the same," he admitted. "Some say they take the form of birds. All know of the little elepaio bird, the one who chooses proper hardwood logs for canoe making."

"I have heard of that one," Paulo agreed. "But my people believe it is the goddess, Laka, who comes as a bird!"

"Aia! My stories must be mixed!" Olu shook his head.

Paulo prompted: "She changes herself into a little bird and runs along the log, remember?"

"That is right," Olu agreed, solemnly.

"If she stops to peck, the log is rotten in that place. Such a trunk would not make a good canoe."

"True, true!"

Paulo warmed to his story. "The canoe could not sail. It would be contrary and probably sink."

Olu's round face broke into a grin. "Nonetheless, I still think the Menehunes could do the same," he insisted.

"You think so?" the boy asked.

"Aia, they are wondrous little men! I know a chant about them." He moved to start the climb. "You like to hear?"

"Yes . . . oh yes!" Paulo answered eagerly.

The big man filled his lungs. When the chant came, it was deep and resonant . . . flowing through the rain forest like chords from a cathedral organ:

In very ancient times,
On the island of Oahu
Jewel of the Hawaii-nei,
A young king was lost.
He came from a distant land.

An angry sea had spewed him forth.
Rough breakers rolled him,
Scratchy sand dried him,
Grasses of the plain clothed him.
But even the royal ones must eat!

The king was very hungry,
His opu was tight and empty.
He wandered toward the mountains
To search for berries and roots
Since, on the great plain was nothing.

This was so long ago, he saw
No village, no people, no taro ponds.
In the mountains, also, was nothing.
No trails nor resting places.
Only gnarled trees and tumbled rocks.

A green cleft in the hills
Drew the weary traveler.
We call it the valley of Manoa.
Even then, it was beautiful.
It promised food and drink.

The king climbed high
Clear to the rain forest.

"This land is rich!" he said.
"I shall claim it as my own."
Who can blame him?

There was no trail.
Rocks were treacherous
And wet with moss.
The royal one slipped
And broke one leg.

He fell down senseless
To a clearing below.
He felt no pain.
The king was alone . . . about to die.
But there was none to see.

A tiny, scarlet bird fluttered
From a branch on a nearby tree.
He had never seen a man thing.
Curiosity filled his eyes.
He hopped close and cocked his head.

It was plain to see, the injury.
A leg was twisted; face pale.
The bird flew high . . .
And returned with a green leaf
Held fast in his sharp bill.

Gently, the bird rested
Fresh-plucked leaf across the bruise
And pecked it

And pushed it tight
To stop the flow of blood.

Like magic the bruises faded.
Then the little bird hopped
To a rock near the young king's face,
Reaching forward to touch
Still lips with pointed bill.

A clap of thunder filled the air.
Bird had changed to man!
A short, bearded, brown,
Dwarf of a man.
In fact . . . a Menehune!

The king awoke
And sprang to his feet.
His leg was mended
And soreness gone.
"Who are you?" he asked.

The dwarf who had been a bird
Stamped both his knobby feet.
"King of the Menehunes!" he roared.
"Your blood is royal . . .
You broke my spell,
Now I must grant a wish!"

"This land is yours?" the young king asked.
"You own it all?"
"All!" the Menehune answered.

"We own the trees, rocks, bushes,
Flowers, animals, insects, birds,
Grass, soil, clouds, rain . . ."

In actual fact . . .
The little dwarf
Named all things
'Til out of breath
And there was nothing left.

"I see," the young king said.
"But you spoke of a wish?"
"True!" the dwarf made ənswer.
"But make your wish now—
I must leave before night's shadows fall."

The king turned to face the sea.
It shone radiant and smooth.
Thoughts of his homeland
Made sad his face.
"I would return to my kingdom," he said.

"Done!" cried the dwarf
As though relieved.
"But . . . go to sleep
Or you will learn my magic!"
The young king did as he was bid
And stretched out upon the rock.

A sound of breakers
Filled his ears.

When eyes were opened
He lay upon the sand.
Blue sky and sun were overhead,
Dark forest was no more.

Atop a wave, a huge canoe
Bore swiftly toward the beach.
A double war canoe
With twelve strong paddlers.
And the young king rubbed his eyes.

This was his own canoe
Just lost beneath the sea!
And his own true paddlers
Stout warriors all,
Returned from a watery grave!

"I have never seen such magic!"
The young king softly whispered.
"The Menehunes of the mountain
Are greatest in the world!
Truly . . . I am in their debt."

He hailed his warriors
And climbed aboard.
None could explain
The great miracle,
Being filled with awe.

Willingly, they headed out to sea.
A land so strange, however beautiful

Was not like home, they argued.
So paddles bent
Spray rose high
And great joy warmed their hearts!

Olu laughed, indulgently.
"Now you have heard the Chant of the Menehunes of Manoa," he said. "You liked it?"

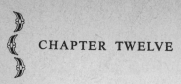

CHAPTER TWELVE

In the Rain Forest

SKIES were darkened now, banked high with thunderheads. Every few minutes, light showers fell. The trail was slushy underfoot. Deep silence covered the rain forest.

Olu's strong body forced the way. Paulo followed behind, hard pressed to see the path. Scratches and small gnats annoyed him. It would be a relief to stop.

"Clearing ahead," Olu panted. "There our work begins."

Abruptly, the trail broke through brush and rocks. Brief sunshine filtered between the branches to show an open glade. Ringed about were lush-growing trees and climbing vines with huge leaves, their roots deep-buried in moss and ferns. Paulo thought of a fairies' circle, tall grass and fragrant flowers forming its soft carpet.

Swiftly he ran into the open, flinging wide his arms.

A startled creeper bird squeaked and was away with a rush of wings. At a distance, a sleepy owl hooted. As Olu caught up to the boy and let drop his carrying pole and the adzes, Paulo spoke in an awed whisper:

"Surely the little Menehunes live here!" he said, still under the spell of Olu's chant.

"May be," Olu agreed, indulgently. "But here also grows the olona."

He flexed his broad shoulder muscles to clear the stiffness and sniffed the damp air. His nose twitched to the dank smell of rotting wood and foliage, and the heavy perfumes of exotic flowers.

Paulo's ears strained to the sound of small movements here and there . . . the wet plop of a green frog as it hopped to a new leaf in a patch of sun . . . eerie moaning of soft winds . . . rubbing branches and rustling, impatient leaves. His perspiring skin grew cold to the damp air, raising thrilling goose-pimples.

Bare feet sank blissfully into the springy grass. It was sheer enchantment.

"Like a . . . a strange dream," he said, aloud.

"Aia! No dream this," Olu said with a deep laugh. "Thorns and blisters will make it real enough!"

He led the way to a thicket of tall-growing olona bushes. After looking them over carefully, he nodded.

"These will do," he said. "I cut and you strip!"

Paulo took the stone adze from Olu's hand. Soon he was engrossed in his task of removing the bark. Olu worked swiftly. A pile of branches were gathered before Paulo had stripped the second pole.

"You haven't the knack!" Olu told him.

Then he showed the boy how to make the first cut. Bark peeled in a glistening damp strip from the wood. With a practiced twist, the man coiled a ring and laid it to one side.

Paulo tried very hard to do the same, wanting to show Olu that he could be a real help. The bark peeled . . . but he got only narrow strips, doubling the work. He kept trying. Soon he had a sizable pile of dark strips lying in a tangle at his feet.

"You do well," Olu encouraged him.

"I get only narrow slivers," Paulo answered.

"Plenty fiber in all! It will make good fish line."

Paulo felt better.

Being of help lessened the sting of the nettle on

his hands. He decided that he liked working with Olu here in the rain forest.

While they worked, thunderheads moved like ponderous giants across the rim of the mountain. Like silver arrows, drops of rain streaked down, sometimes in broad sunshine. It was a wondrous thing how it could be raining and all sunlight at the same time, then in an instant, thick shadow again would cover all. Trees close overhead protected the man and boy from most of the damp.

At length they had a great pile of twisted bark rings to take back to the village. With practice Paulo had been able to do his share. Now, his hands were sticky with sap from the oozing bark. They smarted from numerous jabs and felt limp with fatigue. But he was happy.

Sharing work made Paulo feel closer to the chantmaker. He had done many things now with Olu; traveled, eaten, and slept in the longhouse. Being together like this, in the solitude of the rain forest, established a bond between them. There was less pain in Paulo's thoughts of his lost village and his mother. The dull ache inside was gradually healing.

"Enough!" Olu suddenly exclaimed, throwing his heavy stone adze with a dull thump into the grass at his feet.

Raising his shoulders and stretching his arms to free them of fatigue, Paulo remarked: "I feel dizzy! We must be high up the mountain."

"Not so high," Olu answered with a laugh. "Your small belly is empty again, that's all!"

"I could eat," the boy agreed. Then he looked around. "But we brought nothing!"

Olu laughed, heartily. "We starve, I think!"

From the way he said it, Paulo knew there was another answer. "You know of something," he said.

"I see I can't fool you!" Olu laughed again. "You like some ripe berries? I know the place."

"Berries will be fine," Paulo agreed.

Olu started across the open glade, through the wet grass. "First . . . we wash!" he called back to Paulo.

They found a small rivulet of rain water coursing down a cleft in the rocks. It was cool and sweet with the clean taste of smooth stone and white rootlets. Both drank deeply, then scrubbed their hands with fine sand. Nettle stings and dirt disappeared like magic.

Paulo splashed the big man playfully, then got a good drenching as Olu ducked the boy's head in the running stream. They both smacked their hands against the water in a ceaseless flooding. It was great sport and they were soon dripping wet from head to toe.

"Enough . . . you drown me!" Paulo protested, and escaped to a rock warmed by the fleeting sun.

They found the berries growing at the far end of the clearing.

Both man and boy were soon gorging on the sweet, juicy fruit. Paulo swallowed luscious ripe black ones until he was content to hunt out only the very largest. The feel of bursting juices on his tongue and the crunch of soft pulp between his teeth was a delight.

"We rest a while," Olu said when they had eaten all they could hold. "Then we start down the mountain."

Paulo stretched out full across a warm rock. Olu sat leaning against a gently sloping outcrop. Paulo soon heard low-throated snoring as Olu's head dropped to his chest.

Work was finished. The trail back to the village would be all downhill. It was wonderful just to lie and watch the clouds scud across the blue sky. Thunderheads were changed to white, frothy streamers by the urgent trade wind. Sunlight was brilliant now, and shadows in the surrounding forest deepened in contrast.

Time passed unnoticed.

Paulo was first to throw off his drowsiness, his active young body craving movement. He decided to explore while Olu finished his nap.

While making an almost complete circuit of the open glade, Paulo's attention was caught by each place under rocks and brush. Who knew what might be hidden here? He craned his neck to look high into the tops of trees and rocky crags. Perhaps some ani-

mal might attract his eye before slipping into the surrounding gloom.

One deep, almost lightless pocket in the rocks
made him catch his breath. It could well be the secret
den of the Menehune, he imagined. A short, dark
brown little man seemed to peer at him from the
shadows, scowling at being discovered. Paulo could
swear he had seen the gleam of his eyes in the darkness. A sudden chill raised bumps on the boy's skin.
He shrank back, almost afraid.

"If that were the King of the Menehunes, he
would grant me a wish," he told himself. "I wish that
. . . that . . . what shall I wish?"

Words of the chief Kuokoa came to his mind.
"You have the makings of a fine hunter," the Great
One had said.

Paulo fingered the throwing stone at his waist.
Perhaps, if he tried harder, he could learn its use.
He determined to practice twice as much. And be-
come expert with his new spear, too!

He closed his eyes tight. "I wish . . . to be a great
hunter!" he said, aloud. "Then Kuokoa will let me
stay in Manoa." Paulo wished so hard his face was
all screwed up into a big frown.

When his eyes opened, there was just a dark hole
in the side of the mountain. He felt silly . . . he was
too old to play at such games. But wishing had been
fun. And he felt he had reached a great decision—
he would be a hunter!

Feeling very grown up indeed, Paulo continued his exploring. What had been an empty forest now seemed to be teeming with game. Just ahead, a twisted volcanic rock became a charging wild pig with vicious fangs. The chief, lying helpless with a twisted ankle, was in the wild pig's path. In one swift motion, Paulo loosed his trusty throwing stone and the charging animal lay motionless in a tangling coil of braided hair.

And there, to the right!

Were those dead branches in the brush, or fuzzy ears of a slinking wild dog intent on a bloody capture? Again, the stone whined in protest as it swung a dizzy arc. A marauding beast of the forest lay helplessly snarled in the thicket. No lurking game was safe from Paulo, mighty hunter!

Looking up, something caught the boy's attention. High on a ledge of rock, straggling branches of a strange plant nodded its slender leaves. And among the leaves were brilliant globes of scarlet.

Paulo struggled up the ledge and reached his hands to draw down a branch. Sunlight flashed on the largest, reddest berries the boy had ever seen. All were perfect. No bird had nibbled their ruddy skin, nor worms pierced their plumpness.

Greedily, he cupped one hand and stripped a berry from the bush. It was tart and stung his tongue. But the sensation was a welcome change from the cloying sweetness of the black berries he had eaten.

There were not many scarlet ones, so he soon cleaned the bush.

"What a treat!" he thought.

Then Paulo was sorry he had eaten all without a thought for Olu. Guiltily, he knew he should have shared his find. But perhaps Olu had eaten plenty of such berries on other trips to the rain forest, he reassured himself. A glance toward the rock where the chantmaker was napping showed Olu was now awake and rising to his feet.

"Paulo?" Olu called. "We go!"

"Coming!" the boy answered as he scrambled down the rocks.

Scarlet berries were soon forgotten in his haste to help load the coils of olona bark onto Olu's carry- ing pole.

It was not until they were almost all the way down the mountain and the village was in sight that Paulo faltered. Strange things were happening in his stomach. Writhing snakes seemed to be twisting and turning with great discomfort. Every now and again one bit, sharply! Beads of perspiration were gathered on Paulo's brow. His feet grew heavy . . . keeping up with Olu was suddenly an impossibility.

"Olu!" he called, faintly. "I . . . I feel . . ."

And Paulo stumbled on the trail, to lie quiet where he fell.

CHAPTER THIRTEEN

The Kahuna Practices His Trade

BY THE time Olu carried Paulo down the trail to the men's longhouse, a crowd had gathered.

"What ails the keiki?" friendly voices asked.

"I know not," Olu assured them, his face grave with concern.

Paulo writhed in great pain on his lauhala sleeping mat. Since his collapse on the trail, he was almost unconscious and mumbled senseless things.

"The gods have sent an evil spirit and caused the sickness!" one man assured Olu.

"Aia, it is the dread sorcery! The keiki is dying!" another said with a dismal shake of the head.

Olu was pale with fear and worry. Hadn't the chief Kuokoa placed the keiki in his care? He would be held responsible! He knelt shakily beside the prostrate boy.

"Paulo! Paulo, little one! Tell what happened!" he urged, hoarsely.

The boy rolled over, moaning weakly.

Another man said: "It is the lizard god? See? Even now he chews the keiki's vitals!"

All drew close about the boy. It was true—the small opu was taut and swollen. Olu stood upright, suddenly.

"Beg the Kahuna to attend!" he said, desperately.

"He has been summoned," a voice assured him at his elbow. "See, even now the Great One approaches."

In full priestly regalia of black-feathered cape and loincloth, the Kahuna stalked into the longhouse. At his heels trotted a tall boy, the Kahuna's son and apprentice. The boy carried a large bundle wrapped in printed kapa.

"Make way!" the Kahuna called in a querulous voice.

His wrinkled face was severely expressionless, although his bald head glistened with moisture from his haste. His awesome presence commanding instant respect, the group about the boy's pallet drew back and melted into the shadows of the longhouse, while the Kahuna mumbled incantations and prayers and pushed air with his bony hands. Then, he stood a moment and looked down at Paulo.

"What happened?" he asked Olu, severely.

"I know not, Great One," Olu assured him. "The keiki collapsed on the trail coming from the rain forest."

The Kahuna fingered the grey stubble on his chin, seemingly deep in thought. When at length he spoke, his eyes flashed fiercely.

"The keiki is obviously bewitched!" he said, solemnly.

A gasp of concern escaped the throats of the onlookers. They shrank further back. All knew it was a dreadful thing to be bewitched. Strong magic must be invoked to do battle with the evil spirits. Who could tell where next they might strike? A respectful and fearsome silence filled the longhouse.

Meanwhile, the tall boy spread the contents of

the kapa cloth bundle on the dirt floor. First, the Kahuna took a black bowl, with images carved in full relief at each end, and placed this near Paulo's side. The images were gods with fat bellies and grimacing mouths filled with teeth. From polished wooden bowls and small hand gourds, the Kahuna poured aromatic powders into the gods' bowl. A spicy and irritating odor filled the room. Some of the men mumbled. Whites of eyes gleamed in the darkness.

"Fetch a burning stick!" the Kahuna ordered.

The apprentice ran to obey.

The Kahuna took a short candle made of oily kukuinut meats stuck on a splinter and placed this carefully in the center of the bowl.

All the while, he chanted prayers in a rasping voice.

With the burning stick, he lit the kukui candle.

It spluttered for a moment, then burned with a smoky yellow flame. The shadow of the boy crawled across the thatched walls. It was an eerie scene, inspiring dread and respect in the minds of the superstitious villagers. Olu visibly trembled.

Then the Kahuna knelt beside Paulo. Skillfully, he ran skinny fingers over the taut abdomen. He looked deeply into the boy's rolling eyes and listened to the spasmodic breathing. Knowing hands thumped, probed, and squeezed the writhing body.

Paulo roused to the intimate touch. His bleary eyes opened, his swollen tongue mouthed words. The Kahuna leaned closer.

"B . . . b . . . berries," the boy said, weakly. Then his tousled head lay limp against the mat.

None present could hear the words. But the Kahuna gave a grunt of satisfaction. Swiftly, he pawed the contents of the kapa bundle and brought forth a slender, red-dyed hand gourd. He removed its stopper. Round drops of a clear liquid were measured into a drinking bowl.

Paulo moved slack hands across his stomach.

"It . . . hurts . . . here," he whispered.

With surprising gentleness, the Kahuna administered his potion. He tipped the boy's head and Paulo was forced to swallow the bitter liquid. As it touched his tongue, he grimaced and almost choked.

"Drink!" the Kahuna ordered, crisply.

The boy opened heavy lids to look directly into

the man's face. It was unrelenting. Without further protest, Paulo swallowed the contents of the bowl.

All present sighed with relief. The villagers had great faith in their kahuna.

"Now we shall see," a man whispered in Olu's ear.

"He was in my care," the big man choked.

The Kahuna stayed by the boy's side long into the quiet hours of night. Once, unseen by those present, the Kahuna fingered the carved shell necklace around Paulo's neck. He leaned forward to examine this at close range. A puzzled frown creased his face and his eyes crinkled deeply as the priest held secret communion with his thoughts.

Olu sat on his mat a short distance away, keeping a faithful vigil. Certain men of the village also watched in turn and brought the chantmaker refreshing drinks. None dared approach the Kahuna.

It was a weary time.

The cracked old voice of the Kahuna made a tiresome accompaniment to the noisy splutter of the kukuinut candle.

"He is a good Kahuna, that one," Olu admitted, grudgingly.

After a time, lines of pain left the small boy's face. He quieted and slept. The Kahuna rose stiffly to his feet, joints cracking as he signalled the attendant to gather his belongings.

"The boy's personal god has regained control,"

he said, impressively. He raised a hand to describe a mystic sign in the air. "His ancestors now watch over him. All will be well."

He stalked from the longhouse.

Next morning, Paulo had indeed improved. His eyes were bright and mischievous again. And though very weak, he complained to Olu of being hungry. The big man was delighted.

"Aia! Your opu is a tough one!" he roared with a great laugh. He shoved forward a parcel wrapped in fresh green ti leaves. "Anuhea, my good wife, is wise in the needs of keikis, it seems," he shouted.

His clumsy fingers tore at the binding leaf and exposed milky white squares of a delicacy. Paulo rolled on his side and looked.

"It's . . . it's kulolo!" he whispered, his eyes big with wonder. "Taro and coconut pudding like my mother used to make!"

Shaky fingers reached the biggest square to a mouth that grew moist with anticipation. "I . . . like . . . that!" he mumbled with delight.

"Aia! He eats! The little one eats again!" Olu shouted for all to hear.

The longhouse filled with happy laughter.

CHAPTER FOURTEEN

The Big Fishing Party

PAULO regained strength rapidly but it was several days before he felt himself again. He spent lazy hours practicing with his throwing stone and spear, helping with small chores, and taking long naps under the shade of a big tree near the longhouse.

Then one afternoon Olu sought him out.

"Think you're strong enough to travel?"

"I feel fine!" Paulo said, instantly alert.

"Your sickness is pau—all gone?"

"Pau," the boy answered. "I was greedy, the gods but punished me."

"There are some who would do a little . . . hunting," Olu said with a gleam in his eyes.

"Where?" asked Paulo quickly, patting the throwing stone tucked in his loincloth.

"Near Kou, on the great plain," Olu said.

Paulo asked no further questions. He knew it would not really be a hunting party at all, now that he thought about it and caught the significance of

Olu's manner. What the big man had told him was that they were going fishing.

All knew that fishes have ears!

To say that one was going fishing was kapu for it would be a warning to the wary ones. Reefs would be found deserted by all but useless little wrigglers. So men fooled the fish and called their intentions by another name. Paulo knew there was nothing to hunt on the great plain except big rats, with bow and arrow. He smiled knowingly at Olu.

"Do many go?" he asked.

"Most men of the village. There will be a big party."

Paulo's eyes grew round with excitement.

A fishing party was a community festival, he knew. All would join in catching fish with enormous nets. Afterwards, there would be a feast with chanting.

"I'm ready!" he said.

"Go roll your mat," Olu directed. "I'll collect our small gear."

The village square was filled with excitement and happy laughter. Fresh fish would be welcome. Racks in the smokehouses would be filled again, if the gods were generous.

With happy shouts men of the village raised their fishing spears aloft. Bottle gourds filled with coiled olona fishlines were slung over their shoulders. Big nets were tied to carrying poles, every mesh perfect after weeks of careful mending. Wives handed the men ti leaf packages of food fresh from the steaming ovens. Small keikis tugged at stalwart legs, screaming that they wanted to go and wailing dismally when told to stay at home.

At a distance, Paulo recognized the slight figure of the Kahuna. The important man stood in front of the temple images and called upon the gods to bring good fortune to the hunt . . . and full nets!

Even the chief Kuokoa came out of his high thatched house and watched the preparations from his porch. Paulo knew he would not join the party. Chiefs hunted by themselves, for big gamefish from fast outrigger canoes. Only the villagers, the common folk, engaged in the fishing party. Just the men, of course. Women and small keikis were kapu on the fishing grounds. They must stay indoors in their thatched houses and await the men's return.

Paulo realized that Olu had been generous in allowing him to go. As almost the smallest boy in the group, he resolved to be as helpful as possible.

"Let me carry something," he said when he returned with his bed mat.

Down the trail from the village, men strode in single file. They used a short-cut to the sea. The eager fishermen would travel across the plain and reach the ocean beach by nightfall. Here, those not too excited would sleep and rise at break of dawn for fishing.

Paulo stayed close beside Olu on the trail. Men shouted, sang, or laughed boisterously. Much joking went the rounds as wagers were made on the biggest catch. When the noisy group reached the open plain, men from other villages joined them. Back-slapping, rough play, and exchange of gossip lasted until the shoreline was reached. Soon all were settled for the night in a sprawling camp along the beach. Breakers smashed against outlying reefs to spend themselves in a rush of rolling swells and white froth.

Paulo lay on his mat in a hollow of the sand, wide awake and listening. Olu sat talking with a group of strangers near by. They were just voices in the night, exchanging village gossip.

"Day after tomorrow is the King of Oahu's birthday," the boy heard one man say.

"There'll be much feasting!" another man answered with a laugh.

"The palace will burst its walls!" the first man agreed.

"Are all invited?"

"Not to the palace. But there'll be sports in the daytime."

Olu's deep voice rumbled: "It's the season of the autumn games," he said. "There will be much gambling."

One of the men chuckled knowingly. "Yes, with our tax goods!" he said.

Paulo knew that the autumn games were held

annually. He wondered if he would see any of the sport.

A man asked: "Think you the King will attend?"

Olu answered: "It's customary. All may see and pay him homage."

Paulo's hearing sharpened. "Imagine!" he told himself. "To see the King of Oahu with my two eyes!" He was very glad Olu had brought him along for the fishing party.

One of the men spoke again: "Do you make a chant?" he asked Olu.

Paulo gasped. The chantmaker was known all the way to the other villages!

"I will think on it," Olu answered, diffidently.

"It would be a great thing to make a king's chant," the man persisted.

"Who can say?" Olu answered with embarrassment. "My chants are but play for children."

"Not so! We in our village, clear around the mountain, sing what you have created. Why not a king's chant, then?"

Roll of the heavy night surf drowned out the man's answer.

Next morning, as pink dawnlight rose over the forest-clad mountains, men from all the villages joined nets together. This made one net over a thousand feet long. Never before had Paulo seen such a net! Just to haul it through the surf took two canoes and the strength of all the men and boys.

Ropes of strong fibrous bark, hung with leaves, were used to drag the net. Later these would be used to grapple both net and fish from shallow water to the beach. In places, the net was weighted on the bottom edge with stones. On top, it was floated with logs of very light wiliwili wood. Paulo and Olu waded into the surf to help fasten these floats.

The boy turned to the big man and asked: "There are so many fish, then?"

Olu laughed. "Big net doesn't always mean big catch!" he said wisely.

Paulo thought this net long enough to catch all the fish in the sea. However, time proved the wisdom

of Olu's words. All the first day the sea paid little
for their labors.

Time and again Paulo helped as the long net was
paid out into vast circles across the open roof. But

the catch was scanty. Gods were thwarting them, the men decided.

Fishing was done inside the coral ring that formed a barrier to the line of breakers. Here the water was shallow and fairly calm. It varied in depth from a few feet to a man's shoulders. Men and boys were stationed every few feet around the net. Gradually, they worked their way toward each other until the net was joined to form a circular wall around the fish. Drawn closer, it puckered like a bag. Thus the fish were trapped and slowly dragged to the beach.

Living all his life near the surf, Paulo was much at home in the water. He felt very important, diving here and there to free the net from the rough coral bottom. It was hard work for all. No edge of the net was allowed to sink below the water's surface, else valuable fish would escape and everyone's work would go for nothing.

Fish swim faster than men . . . and are wily, too!

Sometimes, feeding sharks were caught in the circle. Then consternation reigned. All present slapped water and screamed loud protests to distract the menace. Strong swimmers did battle with sharp spears to destroy the marauder before the net was torn or a man injured.

They managed to get enough fish for the feast that night, but none could be smoked for taking back to the villages. There just were not enough fish in the reefs this day.

Paulo was glad when the time came to prepare their supper. Holes had been dug in the sand and lined with stones for temporary cooking ovens. Sweet-fleshed fish from their catch were wrapped in green leaves and slowly baked. Others were prepared raw, to be eaten with spicy sauces. Gourds of poi paste were opened to provide the islanders' bread for the meal.

No one went hungry, but poor catches dampened spirits; the gaiety was only half-hearted.

Long stories were told to pass the time as men and boys settled on their mats. Mostly, they talked about ancient deeds of valor, adventures of the gods, and doings of the fabled royal ones of long ago. Paulo listened to the man-talk as long as his eyes stayed open. But a strenuous day soon sent him to his own sleeping mat.

Tomorrow, perhaps, the gods would send more fish.

The distant roar of surf and murmuring swells as they broke along the reef filled Paulo's ears. He slept.

CHAPTER FIFTEEN

Paulo Goes to the Autumn Games

THE FISHING next morning was more re-
warding.

With the first dawn cast, the net teemed with
splashing fish. By full sun time, wriggling piles lay
gleaming on the beach, and a group of men and
boys left the net to tend smoky fires for quick-curing
their catch.

Paulo helped Olu to gather wood for the fires.

Everyone was happier this day. Many prize fish
had been netted. Stacks of smoked and salted fish
grew high on their beds of fresh ti and banana leaves.
By high sun time, it was decided they had enough
fish for the day.

"The gods will be offended if we are greedy!"
men said. "Let us spend the rest of the day in fun."

Paulo could hear distant shouts of merriment
and sporting from the plain of Kou. He watched as
small groups of villagers deserted net and fish to walk
towards the sports arenas.

"We go?" Paulo asked Olu, hopefully.

"Aia! It's true, we must not be greedy," the big man nodded. "We go see the fun!"

They joined one of the hurrying groups and headed toward the outskirts of the village.

Crowds of people were everywhere.

Most colorful were the royal ones, the chiefs and relatives of the King, in their red and yellow feathered cloaks, crested helmets, and skirt-like loincloths. Stewards of the King and important guests from other islands sat in shaded pavilions in view of all. Haughty warriors guarded their privacy. Not even the shadow of a villager was allowed to cross their path.

"Is one the great King of Oahu?" Paulo asked as he watched the magnificent display.

Olu shaded his eyes from the glaring sun and searched the pavilions.

"Aia, that is the King!" he said, pointing a finger across the clearing. "He with the bright red cloak. See, near the pole with the royal flag."

Olu and Paulo moved as close as they dared.

The King sat surrounded by his court, watching a footrace now in progress. He laughed easily and talked freely with those beside him. Though seated, he looked tall and like a royal one, Paulo thought.

"What a great man," Paulo whispered. "Now my eyes have seen the King of Oahu!"

"Watch the race," Olu prodded, "and learn

much of running. All here are professionals."

Paulo thought of his own contest in the village of Manoa. "How can men run so fast?" he wondered as the race was finished.

While the sun moved slowly across the blue sky, one event after another took place. He shuddered at the brutal lua or "bone-breaking" wrestling: a form of super ju-jitsu. He became excited as he watched the King's sport of spear catching, in which warriors threw spears at each other. The object was to catch in either hand as many spears as possible. Paulo could hardly believe his eyes as one daring man caught three spears in each hand, and trampled a seventh with a stamping foot!

Along the adjoining stretch of beach, outrigger canoes raced toward the shore. The first to touch the sand was declared the winner. Surf board riding came next. On flat, cigar-shaped boards, from seven to sixteen feet long, men rode the incoming breakers. It took great balancing skill to stay on the narrow boards for any distance.

Paulo was fascinated by the ukeke players.

The ukeke was a three-stringed instrument about the size and shape of a foot ruler, played while held against the lips. Beating time was done with the palm of the hand on the pahu or sharkskin covered hollow drum. Rattling gourds and striking sticks added to the rhythm.

Between dances, chants were spoken and sung. It was then that one of the men from the fishing party noticed Paulo and Olu. Watching his chance during a lull in the music, the man shouted: "Let Olu from Manoa make a chant!"

The people hushed at such daring.

A look of annoyance crossed Olu's face and he sought to push back into the crowd. Paulo grabbed the big man's hand, urging him to stay.

"Olu must chant!" the crowd timidly took up the cry.

The King paused in his conversation to take notice. He called one of the guards and appeared to question him. Paulo could feel Olu's arm tremble. They both watched in stunned silence.

At length, the King turned toward the crowd and motioned his assent with a careless wave.

Those nearest pushed Olu forward as the crowd quieted, expectantly.

"Who is this man?" the King called loudly from the shadows.

"I am Olu, Great One," the big man answered. "Some call me the chantmaker."

"You don't look it!" the King called, banteringly. "More like a crusher of rocks, you are!"

The crowd laughed.

"Come, big one, let us hear your voice," the King added.

While the crowd became quiet, the big man studied the ground at his feet. He seemed to be thinking deeply.

Paulo was almost numb with excitement. "Will he make a king's chant?" he asked himself, "or give one known to all?"

Olu drew a deep breath.

All eyes were on the chantmaker when, at length, his powerful voice rolled across the square:

"O mighty Ku!
God of war and power
O mighty Lono!
God of growing things and peace
O mighty Kane!
Creator of all living creatures
And the sacred forest
O mighty Kanaloa!
God of the departed spirits
Hear me now!
Hear me now!

Today is the birthday
Of our beloved King.
We gather to do him honor.
He is our father
Our mother
Our trusted brother
And guardian to all.

His fame has crossed the restless waters
To all the islands of Hawaii nui.
Fishes of the sea fear his strength,
Wild pigs fear his slender lance,
Mighty warriors flee his path,
All know him to be strong and just.
Strong and just!

O mighty Gods of the heavens!
And the fiery depths below!
Let no harm come
To our beloved King.
O ancient Gods of peace and war!
Let our homeland
Our land of plenty
Prosper under his fair hand.

Let none ravish the good earth
Nor redden the bountiful sea
Nor darken the blue heavens
Nor bring sickness or death
To this, our island of Oahu
Paradise on earth.
This is our prayer
For the birthday
Of our good King.
Hear us, O mighty ones!
Hear us!
We have spoken."

Olu bowed with dignity, and waited.

As the big man's voice spoke the last words, all eyes turned toward the King. Paulo slipped his small hand into Olu's palm and pressed it fervently. He was so proud!

In the shaded pavilion, the King rose to his feet. From around his neck, he removed a beautiful lei, a garland of yellow flowers—the King's own color and royal token of Oahu.

"Come forward, chantmaker!" he ordered with a smile.

Olu loosed his hand from Paulo's grasp. With eyes lowered, he approached the King and knelt to one knee and bowed his head.

The King lowered the garland until it hung about the big man's neck. Then he faced the people.

"We are greatly pleased with this man," he said in a loud voice. "He has made a chant to do us

honor. Let him henceforth be called 'Chantmaker to the King'!"

A mighty cheer sounded from the crowd. The people were delighted. The King had made a gracious gesture and bestowed on one of his subjects great honor! Olu was congratulated from all sides.

"You made a king's chant!" Paulo cried. "Now the chief Kuokoa will be proud of you!"

A grin spread over Olu's face. Nervous fingers raked his hair, then plucked at the garland of flowers. Paulo could see the chantmaker felt relieved and pleased at the same time.

"Aia!" the big man agreed. "I must have been bewitched. Anuhea will never believe I could be so bold!"

The day's games ended with a hula dance performed in front of the King's pavilion. Both men and women, specially trained, took part in the graceful dances, with music and chanting accompanying them.

CHAPTER SIXTEEN

The Rich Haul

NEXT MORNING Olu and Paulo rose at dawn. There were fish still to be caught for the storehouses. However, other fishermen were not so faithful. The autumn games in Kou had been too much for them. They lay snoring on their mats, leaving the work to those more willing.

"You must help like a man today," Olu told Paulo. "Think you can handle the net?"

Paulo was none too sure. But, "I'll try, Olu," he answered.

Staying with the net throughout the casting and hauling was different from diving to free it from the bottom. He must work in deeper water, for one thing, while supporting the weight of the net and helping to gather in its water-soaked folds. It was a difficult job.

"Be careful!" Olu cautioned as they waded. "Stay beside the ropes."

The long net was stretched out across the reef

shallows until a huge circle was made. Paulo found that tugging at the awkward lines took all his strength. However, pulling and straining with a will, he felt that he belonged—the villagers accepted him as equal.

First and second settings of the net went well.

The fish were not yet running strong, but enough were caught to start things going. Everyone was hard at work hauling and tumbling the catch onto the sandy beach. Fires spurted thick clouds of smoke as green brush and leaves were piled high.

"More fish come!" Olu predicted enthusiastically. "We take home plenty!"

With the next cast of the net, Paulo knew his friend was right. Even as they formed a circle, a splashing school of feeding fish swam right into their great purse. Everyone stopped to let the net bob in the water. Soon all the fish were inside.

"What a fuss they make!" Paulo called to Olu.

Large fish and small streaked between his legs. Salt water splashed in his face as the fish rose to the surface. Soon a great circle was boiling with the catch; the whole school was trapped.

"Best haul yet!" Olu called. "When these are taken, we go home!"

Everyone shouted with happiness over their good fortune.

"Never have I seen such a netful!" one man called.

All those who heard answered with a cheer. Each man gave excited directions to the other.

Paulo hung onto the net rope with all his strength. Water here was over the boy's head. And the wili-wili floats were not sufficient to keep the net at the surface. He kicked hard with his legs and struggled to raise the rope.

The fish seemed to know they were trapped. They made long sweeps back and forth across the circle, frantically seeking a way of escape. A few leaped over the net and were gone. However, this was to be expected. They could not capture all the fish.

At the height of the excitement, Paulo's attention was caught by a huge, slow-swimming sea turtle. Deep in the green water, the lumbering creature was heading directly for the boy's section of the net. Through the clear swell, he could see brown and green splotches of the turtle's plated back. Clawed feet paddled water with graceful sweeps and long wrinkled neck stretched forward as beady eyes and sharp beak pointed the way.

"What a prize!" the boy thought with delight, knowing that sea turtle meat was a rare and tasty treat!

Paulo instantly decided that he must manage to trap the turtle. "A surprise for Olu!" he told himself, happily. But how could he manage to get the turtle to swim into a closed net? Dare he lower the edge just enough to allow the prize to swim past the barrier? It would be a risky thing to do, he fully realized. Yet, to capture such a prize without laying a hand on it!

Paulo watched as the turtle swam relentlessly and slowly forward. In an instant its sharp beak

would come smack against the mesh of the net, or be lost as it swerved aside. The boy glanced toward the busy men. Olu was yards away. If he took time to call for help, the turtle would be gone before anyone could swim to his side.

Paulo looked deep into the water. "What shall I do?" he asked himself, helplessly. He could almost stare into the creature's gold-flecked eyes. Their lids winked in ludicrous slow motion. Dark lines on the turtle's horny-plated back were clearly visible. It was almost up to the net.

Paulo could not resist the temptation. In a swift dive, he carried the edge of the net deep into the water. He was none too soon! The bulky shape floated right past his face . . . one clawed foot just missing Paulo's nose. "It must weigh more than a man!" he calculated as it passed. In an instant, the sea turtle glided inside the circle of milling fish.

Greatly elated, Paulo tried to raise the net rope. But now, tension of the circle and surge of current made it unmanageable. He found the rope too heavy to lift to the surface. Desperately, his fingers slipped and strained at the meshes of the clumsy net. They were drawn taut as the string of a bow. Paulo's lungs began to labor—he must rise to the surface for air.

"Olu!" he gasped as his head bobbed out of water. "Help . . . Olu! The net!"

However, Paulo was too late; sharp-eyed fish had spotted the gap!

Silver streaks and splotches of brilliant colors flashed past the boy as the circling fishes started an escape over the net in a continuous stream. Paulo was helpless to stop them. A whole sea of rushing shapes seemed to be heading for him and open water. He kicked his feet, frantically fighting to stay afloat and escape the rush.

With eyes, nose, and ears filled with chop and flying spray, he listened as cries of alarm filled the air. Paulo knew the others now realized the catastrophe.

"What have I done? What have I done?" he thought in horror.

Olu's strong arm closed about his chest.

"What happened?" the big man choked as he

flailed water and drew Paulo to one side. "Are you hurt?"

"No, oh no!" Paulo choked. "I . . . I tried to . . ."

"Wait!" Olu yelled in his ear, and Paulo felt himself being towed through the water by the man's powerful strokes.

Pandemonium had broken loose.

Everywhere in their path, men were struggling with the great net, trying to bring it back to the surface. Boiling fish spilled through the gaps in the circle as the largest catch of the day escaped toward the open sea.

On the beach, Olu and the boy sat catching their breaths.

"Now . . . tell me!" Olu's voice was urgent.

Between anguished gasps for breath, Paulo told about the sea turtle. How he had lowered the edge of the net . . . and could not lift it. Olu stared at him, unbelievingly.

"I . . . I wanted . . . to catch him . . . for you!" Paulo sobbed. "I thought . . . I could . . . lift the rope . . ."

"But we had plenty!" Olu said, dully. "Our biggest catch."

"I know . . . I know! I just thought . . . I wanted . . . Oh, Olu!"

The big man's features looked drawn and tired. "Well, little one, you meant no harm," he said, kindly. "All have to learn."

Villagers had gathered in a group about them. Paulo knew they must have heard his story. Knowledge of the certain disgrace burned his cheeks.

Olu rose slowly to his feet and turned to face the group.

"He's but a *keiki!*" he told them, warningly. "It was a man's job to tend the net. Some here," he looked at them, darkly, "shirked their duty!"

No one spoke as the group parted.

Olu gave the boy's shoulder a pat and strode heavily back to the water. Paulo was left sitting on the sand alone. A few more attempts were made with the net, but heart had gone from the task. Fish had now become wary. "We take what we have and go home," the men agreed. No one approached or scolded Paulo, nor mentioned the big haul. But the boy knew how they felt.

And the sea turtle? No one but Paulo ever saw it!

CHAPTER SEVENTEEN

The House-raising

TIME dragged for Paulo after the return from Kou. Again the village of Manoa seemed a strange place and the boy no part of its activity. He felt disgraced and lonesome.

True, the villagers treated him well. No one mentioned loss of the big haul in his presence, nor complained of the small stores of smoked fish in the storehouses. But Paulo knew he had committed a grave error with the net. He could see by their averted glances and studied politeness that many blamed him. He even imagined that they resented his presence in the village. Now he was not sure he should stay in Manoa. Even Olu seemed distant and less friendly.

Actually, ever since their return, Olu had been thinking of more important matters. Concern over his family's crowded quarters worried the big man.

Altogether, these were not happy days for Paulo. He kept to himself and roamed about the valley trying to find new interests. He continued to practice with his treasured throwing stone and short spear, but his pleasure in their use was blunted. Who now would help him become a great hunter? Paulo spent long hours seated on an outcrop of rock near the entrance to the valley.

From here, he could see distant breakers rolling in from the blue sea. In white, straggling lines across the horizon they broke one after the other. The broad plain seemed vast, empty, and unfamiliar. His mind travelled back to his friend Boki, the trader, and the day when Boki found him alone in the ruined village on the distant island of Maui. Paulo brooded anew over the loss of his mother and friends. He missed them more keenly than ever before.

"What is to become of me?" he asked the passing wind.

Meanwhile, in the village the Kahuna had come into the busy square, asking if anyone had seen the chantmaker. Anuhea and the children were rushing about trying to find the big man.

"Olu, come!" they called. "The Kahuna wants you!"

Paulo returned just in time to see the chantmaker and the Kahuna meet. Olu stood tall and straight before the shrivelled old man.

"You sought me?" the chantmaker asked, coldly.

A crooked smile accompanied the crafty gleam in the Kahuna's eyes. "You have won fame in Kou, it seems," he said with a note of derision in his voice. "Chantmaker to the King, we now must call you!"

Olu's face grew red, but he said nothing.

Paulo stood at a distance and listened. He wondered what business the Kahuna had with Olu.

"News of this has come to the chief Kuokoa," the old man continued. "We have consulted and reached a decision." He paused, impressively, as though expecting some comment from the big man.

Olu stood quietly waiting. Only by a slight twitch of his lips did he betray his inner thoughts.

"What then?" he asked.

"We have consulted omens and read the stars," the Kahuna went on. "The moon is in the proper quarter. The gods have not dissented. All augurs well."

"Yes?"

"Tomorrow your new men's house will be started."

"You mean . . . ?" Olu's eyes widened in disbelief.

"It is Kuokoa's order!" the Kahuna explained, as though assuring this man that it was no idea of his own. "A present from our Great Chief!"

He turned to raise a bony hand in a gesture which included all present. Paulo moved closer, mouth gaping with amazement.

"Hear me!" the Kahuna began. "The Great Chief orders all men of the village of Manoa to help in the

house-raising for the Chantmaker to the King! Woods-
men will go into the sacred forest and cut the ridge-
pole eight paces long; the long posts, two paces long;
and the small cross poles, one pace long. All timbers
for the house must be of sound wood."

He paused to look about, impressively.

"Women will gather good pili grass for thatch-
ing. Keikis will gather pebbles for the floor. Everything must be of the best. It is the chief's order!"

He turned back to Olu.

"I shall cut the piko of the house and say the
prayer when it is done."

Paulo knew that the piko was a tuft of grass left
over the doorway, a magic symbol used to bless a
new dwelling. He was dumbfounded by the honor to
be given the chantmaker. Such a house was for the
Royal Ones!

Olu recovered voice to speak.

"Aia! A magnificent men's house!" he said.

By now the old man was fired with enthusiasm
for his own importance in the great event. His voice
was almost genial when he agreed: "As well built
as though for the chief himself!"

"Indeed, it is a generous present!" Olu said,
dazedly.

The Kahuna watched the chantmaker with envy
watering his rheumy eyes. "To be Chantmaker to the
King is a great honor. The whole valley is proud of

you." He paused, as though words stuck in his teeth. "Our . . . eminent son."

"I am grateful," Olu said with dignity.

The Kahuna turned on his heel to leave. "Tomorrow at sunrise I will choose the site and make the blessing," he said. "It is a wondrous thing for the lowly to rise in the esteem of their neighbors! Your family gods must be pleased!"

All present could tell the Kahuna's tongue was coated with bitter salt.

For three days the whole village joined in the project. Each gave ungrudgingly of his labor. All liked the big chantmaker. None envied his good fortune except the Kahuna, his rival in making chants.

A site for the house was chosen on high ground near the chief's courtyard, a place where all would know of the owner's importance. Stout timbers were cut to length with sharp stone adzes. A tremendous quantity of long pili grass was spread to dry in the hot sun. Worn pebbles were chosen for their smoothness, to make a hard, clean floor. Many balls of braided and twisted sennit cord were needed to lash together the frame. Soon, a strong skeleton was outlined against the sky.

Paulo helped wherever possible.

In the general excitement, the recent fishing party was forgotten by all save the boy. A guilty conscience spoiled his pleasure. Only love for his friend gave

Paulo courage to join the others. He worked hard and faithfully at any task, wanting so much to belong to the village and be loved and respected. Nevertheless, Paulo felt that the villagers were disappointed in him, still considered him a stranger.

With surprising ease, many hands working together soon completed the house. Long pili grass was bunched and carefully laid in tiers across the roof and sides, then securely tied in place. Over the whole house, fish nets were tightly stretched so the pili grass would cure flat and be evenly spread. The piko was set in place above the low doorway.

All agreed this was indeed a magnificent house. Larger than most, it would house the chantmaker and his sons with spacious comfort. Paulo wished that he might live in the new dwelling, then rejected the thought as being impossible. Certainly Olu had said nothing about taking the boy from the men's longhouse.

The interior of the new thatched house was furnished with Olu's simple possessions. Sleeping mats of fresh-woven lauhala were laid on the clean pebble floor. Folded new kapa cloth covers were ready. A new calabash for water, another for poi, together with wooden bowls for eating, were presents from the villagers. Fresh green ti leaves filled with taro, potatoes, salt, dried fish and other delicacies were placed neatly by the doorway as the people filed by.

All was ready for the blessing by the Kahuna.

Early that morning, Paulo had gone off by himself to climb high up the trail toward the rain forest. Here among the ferns and twisting vines, the boy had gathered rare and fragrant leaves. With these, he strung a beautiful garland. Difficult to find, the highly scented leaves were a mark of high esteem in the Hawaiian islands.

Now Paulo watched for a chance to see Olu alone.

He hoped the big man would wear the garland for the house blessing ceremony. But doubts assailed the boy; perhaps Olu would not accept such a present from a keiki. Others more highly thought of might make the gesture of love and friendship. He was tempted to run and hide the garland in the brush and say nothing.

Olu was so excited he dashed about trying to help with all manner of last-minute chores. Men chided him with hearty laughs.

"Your clumsy hands do more harm than good!" they told him.

Olu's wife, Anuhea, and his seven young keikis stood in a group at one side. Fresh-scrubbed faces were round with pride. While Anuhea chatted with her friends, she swore she would turn the big man out of his new house and have it for herself! All knew she was joking to hide her pleasure and satisfaction.

Olu came toward Paulo with an armful of wood

for the new cooking oven. The boy bolstered his courage and stood in the chantmaker's path.

"What then, little one?" the big man asked with a merry chuckle.

"I have this for you," Paulo mumbled with embarrassment. He brought the scented garland from behind his back and held it high for Olu to see.

"Aia!" The chantmaker's mouth opened with surprise. "For me?"

Paulo's round eyes were filled with worship. "For you . . . I gathered them," he said.

Olu tossed aside the wood to kneel before the boy. His face grew serious as his head bowed. Paulo slipped the fragrant garland about the big man's neck. When the strand had settled, Olu raised his head to look deeply into Paulo's soft brown eyes.

"Even the King did not please me more!" he said.

Paulo's cheeks flushed. "You're not angry with me?" he asked.

"I angry? With you?" A gentle smile lit Olu's face. "Little one, I love you like a son," he said, softly. "You dream of anger. There is none in my heart!"

The big man's arm encircled the boy.

"I'll wear your gift for the house blessing. And then—you know what?"

Paulo's lashes glistened with happy tears. "No . . . no. What?"

"I hang it in my new house right beside my mat! It will guard my sleep. No evil spirit will dare approach its fragrance!"

The boy's knuckles wiped damp eyes as he sniffled and tried to smile. "Oh . . . Olu!" His chin quivered. "Must I stay alone?"

"Alone?"

"In the longhouse with the others?" Paulo turned his head. "Perhaps . . . you don't want me."

"Didn't you know?" Olu asked. "Your mat is even now laid in the new house! You sleep with my sons. At least, until Kuokoa decides what must be done."

"It's true? I stay with you?"

"Aia! I would not have it otherwise!"

Paulo was so relieved and happy, his eyes flooded with tears.

They were interrupted by a call: "The Kahuna comes! Make way for the Kahuna!"

Olu rose to his feet, towering above the boy. "Dry your tears, little one!" he said. "No sadness must dampen my new house. All must go right, else the gods will be displeased."

The chantmaker's words comforted the boy.

When they drew near the house, they saw that a crowd was gathered waiting for the blessing. Paulo stood as close to Olu as he dared.

The Kahuna took his place in front of the doorway. His lean face was severely set into a frown of importance as one hand flourished a stone adze. In the other, he held a small, carved wooden image from the temple. After long prayers and incantations, he praised the villagers for their work on the new dwelling. Then at the proper time, the Kahuna cut the piko, left over the doorway, with sharp strokes of the adze.

With the cutting of the tuft, the Kahuna chanted:

> "The servant of the gods
> Cuts the piko

Of the house of Olu,
Renowned chantmaker
To the King of Oahu.
He stands!
He cuts!
The piko is cut.
It is cut down!

Cut is the piko,
The shedder of rain.
A shelter from water
Of the flooding heavens.
Cut is the piko of your house,
O Olu, mighty maker of chants.

Life to the house-dweller,
Life to the guest,
Life to the King,
Life to the chief Kuokoa,
Continue the life of your house
O Olu, mighty maker of chants.

Life to advanced old age,
'Til the eyes are dim,
To the last stages of decay,
'Til borne in a hammock.
The prayer is offered.
It is free."

The house was ready for the new owner!

Olu and his three young sons filed into the shadowy interior. At the doorway, the big man turned, beckoning to Paulo.

"Come!" he said.

CHAPTER EIGHTEEN

The Owl From Thunder Mountain

AFTER moving into the new house, Olu had little time to devote to the newcomer in his home. Not that he neglected Paulo. It was just that his own boys had much to learn; attention must be divided and there were many new chores to keep him busy. Since he now had his own men's house, many things were kapu to women of his family.

The big man must now prepare all the food for himself and his sons; pound poi, tend the cooking oven, clean the house. His wife, Anuhea, was busy caring for his daughters in the old thatched house. There would now be only certain times prescribed by custom and religious law, when Olu could visit with his wife and daughters.

In addition to the household duties, there was always the olona bark to be soaked, then scraped to make fibers for fishlines and nets. This was a tedious job and one of Olu's duties to the village.

Also, he must help friend and neighbor when occasion demanded.

"Aia! I need four hands these days!" Olu often complained.

Paulo, as the oldest boy in the home, was always busy. Only in late afternoon was he free to wander about the village paths and trails. Then the evening meal was not yet taken from the cooking oven, but chores for the day were usually completed.

One afternoon about a week after moving into the new house, Paulo was strolling near the chief's courtyard. His cherished throwing stone rested in its usual place, tucked into the waistband of his loin-cloth.

Beside the staked enclosure, he stopped and smiled ruefully. He remembered his adventure with the new spear, the time he broke the chief's yellow water gourd. He had been more careful since! He looked about the court hoping for a glimpse of the Great Chief. No one was in sight, neither the regular guards nor any of the chief's family. They must be eating, he concluded.

Nearest the mountain side the border of the chief's courtyard ended in a grove of trees, brush, and tumbled boulders. No stakes were needed here since the rough growth formed a natural barrier. Paulo scrambled over the rocks to reach a trail above. As he climbed, a small movement in the courtyard below caught his attention.

He paused and looked more closely.

He was amazed to see one of the chief's small keikis crawling on all fours toward the rocks. "That's unusual," Paulo thought. "The keiki must have crept from that doorway!"

He was tempted to cry out a warning, fearing the child was strayed. Then he thought better of it, realizing his own presence so near the courtyard would have to be explained. No doubt the keiki was in someone's view, he decided, turning back toward the trail.

The keiki's progress was being watched, certainly, but by no one in the chief's household! High overhead on the topmost branch of a slender tree, a large owl from thunder mountain was perched. Intently, the bird lowered his tufted head, and piercing eyes noted the keiki's movement.

Far below, chubby legs and arms worked their way across the clearing. To the bird of prey, the keiki must have looked like a fat suckling pig; a delicious prospect for an evening meal! The keiki paused in its awkward crawl, right out in the open. Round head turned this way and that while innocent eyes looked at the big world.

With a dull swoosh of extended wings, the big owl left his high perch to begin a wide circling in the air. Silently, the broad wings rose and fell. No warning sound of the menacing approach could reach either Paulo or the strayed child.

Lower and tighter the turns became.

Meanwhile, thoughts of the keiki troubled Paulo as he continued his climb over the rough boulders. He paused again to look towards the clearing. From here, the keiki was but a pebble throw below. Paulo was still undecided whether to go on his way or risk calling out a warning.

A shadow slid across his cheek.

Paulo took no notice.

The owl's silent flight came between boy and setting sun; its shadow crossing again.

This time, Paulo looked up.

Instant alarm squinted his eyes as he strove to

see against the glare. As a dark outline, the owl's broad wings quivered in slow descent. The creature stretched its long legs downward and extended sharp claws. Intent on the prey below, the bird seemed unaware of the boy's presence.

In horror, Paulo realized the owl was dropping to grab the keiki in its claws!

With frantic fingers he tore the throwing stone from his loincloth. Its cord of braided hair shivered to the ground. Paulo did not know how he could snare a flying bird, but he knew he must try. "Oh, Boki, good friend . . . help me now!" he prayed. Holding his breath, Paulo slid carefully down a rock to gain a better footing.

From here, the great owl's claws were on a level with Paulo's head. Baleful eyes caught sight of the boy and cruel beak parted in an unearthly shriek as the owl recognized an enemy. Sheer terror chilled Paulo's blood as he raised an arm to shield his face. For an instant it looked as though the owl would check its descent to attack the boy. Wing feathers trembled, but the owl drifted angrily by.

Paulo knew he must act at once. In an instant the owl would have his supper, as even now needle-sharp claws were opened above the keiki's plump body.

Paulo gave a wide swing to the braided cord. "Let my aim be true!" he whispered through whitened lips. Then he loosed the throwing stone with a mighty lunge.

Like a bolt from the sky, the stone head caught the owl's middle and jarred the great bird's descent. Wicked claws tore across the keiki's back and were buried in the ground like a sprung trap. The braided cord tangled in beating wings and flailing legs as the great owl rolled in the dust. With body rumpled and wings dragging, the stunned owl clawed the earth. But the stout cord held him fast.

Foolishly, Paulo rushed down the rocks to reach an eager hand toward the child.

But this was a tough old owl from thunder mountain!

Stunned as it was, the owl would fight for its life. Sharp talons raked Paulo's arm and his hand couldn't reach the keiki. Searing pain almost made the boy faint as he turned to face the owl. Baleful yellow eyes glared into his as ruffled feathers rose and fell and the huge bird panted for breath. Paulo's blow had but partially stunned the creature. It tried, desperately, to strike again.

Paulo wanted to turn and run. "What if the coils come loose?" he thought in a panic.

Suddenly, he realized that to save the child, he must kill the owl. Remembrance of Boki, the trader's words flooded his mind: "One does not kill to prove he is brave!" and the boy was troubled. But this was different, he knew. The keiki was still in danger, the owl a formidable foe. "Help!" he cried as loudly as he could. "Help! Somebody come!" Yet, even as he called, he knew he could not wait.

Frantically, Paulo looked about for another weapon. A large round stone caught his eye. His trembling fingers lifted it and he advanced on the menacing bird. Now the owl's wings were free. They beat the air in an attempt to rise. Paulo moved in close. The owl lunged to bite at his legs and feet with its sharp beak. Paulo cried aloud with the pain. Straining both hands, he raised the stone high above his head and struck.

A dreadful scream came from the owl as the blow descended. Cruel talons raked Paulo's legs as he bashed the stone squarely down on the creature's head. With a sickening thump, the dread owl from thunder mountain was crushed beneath the blow. Lids closed over the baleful eyes. Its body quivered, then the bird lay still.

Through heavy throbbing in his ears, Paulo heard the keiki wailing. Loud voices and cries of alarm added to the clamor. Running feet pounded the ground. Help was coming, at last!

It must have been a terrible sight that met the chief's eyes as he came upon the scene. His youngest keiki was screaming, woefully. Raw scratches crossed its naked back. Paulo's arm was dripping blood and the boy's feet and legs were a maze of oozing scratches. The great owl was a crumpled mass of loosened feathers; with wings, legs, and body now helplessly entangled by the cord.

Leaning against a boulder, Paulo was beyond speech. The boy sobbed with relief as he tried to regain his breath. His face grew pale, then he fainted dead away.

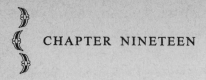

CHAPTER NINETEEN

A Lonesome Day

NEXT morning Paulo awoke as from a nightmare to blink his eyes against glare from the open doorway.

"I am on my own mat," he told himself, dazedly.

Wrappings covered his arms and legs. Soreness filled his body and it was painful to move. His head felt dizzy as he tried to sit upright and clear his mind. Paulo remembered that all through the night his dreams had been filled with the great owl and the helpless keiki. He tried to recall what had happened at the finish.

The owl was dead and the keiki saved, he knew.

Then there had been the deep voice of Kuokoa as the chief shouted orders. And, he remembered someone carrying him to Olu's house. He recalled the sharp pain as the Kahuna dressed his wounds, the relief as cool poultices soothed the cuts. And then he had swallowed the sleep-inducing drug from the bowl the Kahuna held to his lips.

That was all that came clearly.

"My throwing stone was a true weapon," he told himself, shakily. "I wish Boki could have seen me." He wriggled his toes beneath the tight wrappings, then winced as he raised an arm. "Much has happened since I last saw Boki!" he thought, wistfully.

Paulo knew he was the same boy who had crossed the plain from Kou. Yet . . . he felt so different! Things had not turned out as he had expected, but much had happened. Important things, he felt. Here in the valley called Manoa, he had learned to use his throwing stone and the spear, knowing he must be a hunter. He had helped Olu and been to the rain forest, seen Olu's new house raised. He had been to the fishing party and heard the big man make the King's chant at the autumn games in Kou.

Paulo felt much older, more grown up. But his breath stuck in his throat as he thought of the sea turtle and loss of the big catch.

Now, though, hadn't he done battle with the vicious owl? He hoped the keiki was not too badly scratched by the owl's long claws. Would he ever forget those claws? He wondered what Olu thought about the battle. His fingers searched the matting beside the wall. Then he remembered! His precious throwing stone had been left with its cord wrapped about the owl.

"I must get it back!" he said aloud.

Paulo struggled to his feet. His legs were awkward in their wrappings and his arms felt like stumps. He limped out into the sunlight. It was a surprise to see Olu's eldest son, Epo, tending the cooking oven.

"Where is Olu?" he asked as he shakily sat on a near boulder.

Epo looked up, his big, childish eyes sparkling; "You awake?" he asked. "The big one is gone." He laughed as he looked Paulo over. "You are like the worm that spins inside his cover!"

"That's how I feel," Paulo agreed with a grimace. "Where then, is Olu?"

"The Great Chief sent him away."

This was strange news!

"The chief . . . Kuokoa?" Paulo asked.

"Last night the Great One summoned my father."

"What for?"

Epo shrugged small shoulders; "Who knows?" he asked, turning to place another green banana leaf on the cooking oven. "After the Kahuna came to care for you, my father left for Kou," he chattered. "I must take care of the house and my brothers. See, I alone am preparing our food."

Paulo was surprised. "Olu went to Kou? Whatever for?" he asked.

"Father told us nothing. Only that the Great One was sending him." Epo shoved a bowl filled with poi toward Paulo. "You eat something?" he asked.

Absently, Paulo reached down and began spooning the thick white paste into his mouth. "A strange thing," he said.

"Eh?" Epo turned his head to stare. "You do not like the poi?"

"Oh . . . yes! I meant, it's strange, the chief sending Olu away like that."

Paulo was disappointed. Now he must wait to tell the big man about his fight with the owl. He wondered why the chief sent Olu all the way to Kou, and in the night time, too!

"Does he stay?" he asked Epo.

"No. Home by sundown."

Paulo could make nothing of the news.

He spent the day lying on the warm rocks. It was good to lie in the sun and be lazy. Trade wind fanned his cheek with a cooling touch. Gradually, stiffness left his body. Only the smarting of his cuts reminded the boy of the owl's attack. Men of the village walked by his rock on one errand or another. Not seeing the boy lying there, one group argued as they passed:

"I still say he brings no luck!" Paulo heard a man say.

"Because he spilled the net?" another protested. "I don't agree! That was a man's task. The keiki was trying to help!"

"May be," a third man said, doubtingly. "But

what about the owl's attack? All know owls are friendly!"

Paulo was startled. They were talking about him,

he realized. He lay tense, listening.

"To attack the chief's keiki—how terrible!" the first man said.

"Think you the owl might have been bewitched?"

"Such a thing never happened before."

"Not until this stranger came to Manoa," the third man agreed. "The boy brings no luck, I say. What do we know of him? First the fish and now the chief's keiki. I don't like it!"

"You're a superstitious fool! He saved the keiki, didn't he?"

"Think you the chief will let the boy stay in the village?"

Voices blurred in the distance.

Paulo was stunned.

What a thing to say, to blame him for the owl's attack! It was true, then, what he had imagined. There were those in the village who were angry over the fishing party and the lost catch. They resented his presence in Manoa. All things bad were to be blamed on him, it seemed.

Paulo brooded anew over his aloneness. Olu had taken him in, but others were not inclined to be so charitable toward a stranger.

Hours were long and the world a dismal place by the time the red sun set.

CHAPTER TWENTY

An Unexpected Visitor

ACROSS the floor of the valley, the chantmaker's deep voice announced his return. Paulo, low in spirit, his worries a tangled knot within his mind, slipped away to the thatched house, trying to postpone the meeting.

He had reached a decision.

Since chief Kuokoa had spoken no word, the boy was determined to leave the valley of Manoa. Perhaps in Kou he could find a home. Wasn't he strong and willing? Someone would give him food and lodging in return for chores he might do. No longer was he a helpless keiki! If he could face a vicious owl, then he could face the world, he reasoned. Some way, somehow, he would become a mighty hunter. Perhaps for the King of Oahu himself!

In the darkness of the empty house, Paulo's lips quivered. His eyes smarted. It would be hard to tell Olu of his plan to leave. He loved the chantmaker!

Dimly, Paulo could hear a commotion in the vil-

lage square. People were always glad to see the
chantmaker, he thought. Remembering his own ar-
rival, coming down the steep trail by Olu's side, how
beautiful was the valley called Manoa. How thrilling
it had been when Olu made the chant of welcome.
And now, what disappointment.

It was like rocks of salt in his poi!

A clamor accompanied the chantmaker as he
approached.

"Halloo!" he called. "Is there no one to bid me
aloha in my own house? Paulo? Epo? Mali? Keiki
Popo?"

The children were gathered by the cooking oven.
"Coming, Father!" Epo called as they all scampered
to their feet.

"Aia! A fine aloha nui!" Olu chided. "Present
yourselves. We have a guest!"

In the dark interior, Paulo raised his head. "A
guest? Who can it be?" he asked himself. He was disappointed. Now, he would have to postpone telling
Olu of his decision to leave Manoa.

The chantmaker stopped near the doorway to the
thatched house; "Paulo?" he called, then turned to
face Epo. "Can the little one walk?" he asked.

Paulo realized he must act as though nothing had
happened; "I come!" he called through the curtain.
Limping from his bandages, he went outside. "Aloha
nui!" he said as he raised his head.

Then Paulo stood transfixed; dark eyes widening

in disbelief. Standing beside Olu was a familiar figure.

"Boki!" the boy gasped. "Boki, my good friend!"

The chantmaker grinned as he moved to one side. "He comes all the way from Kou," Olu said. "I caught him as he was ready to leave the island."

"Boki, it's really you!" Paulo sobbed. "I've missed you so!"

Boki hugged the boy's head to his chest. "Yes, little one, it's really me!" he answered with a pleased chuckle. "Surprised, eh?"

"Oh, Boki! Take me away, Boki!" he sobbed. "Oh, take me away from here!"

"What's this?" asked the trader in surprise. "You want to leave Manoa?" He turned questioning eyes toward Olu.

The chantmaker's broad shoulders shrugged. "I do not understand," he said.

"I must go," Paulo went on. "No one wants me here!"

"Now, now, little one," Boki soothed. "You're excited by my coming. You but imagine you're not wanted!"

A puzzled frown creased Olu's brow. He drew close to lay a hand on the boy's shoulder.

"What has happened? You know I love you like a son," he said. "Remember? I told you so!"

Paulo sensed pain in the man's voice. He raised a tear stained face. "It's the others," he groaned. "They

say . . . they blame me for losing all the fish . . . and the owl's coming. They blame me!"

"You dream, boy!" Olu protested. "You're ill!"

"No. I heard them talking!"

"Aia! What fool could say such a thing! When did this happen?"

"T . . . t . . . today!"

"It was but idle chatter!"

Olu was obviously disgusted and embarrassed in front of Boki. He turned to the trader.

"The attack of the owl—and now this excitement is too much for the keiki," he said.

The trader motioned for Olu to be silent and led Paulo toward the rocks near the cooking oven.

"Come, little one! We sit and talk!" he said. "You have much to tell me and I have much to tell you."

"First we eat!" Olu stood up and rubbed his stomach. "I know, the keiki's belly is empty!" he added. "Always this one gets strange ideas when he's hungry. Never have I seen such a troublesome little belly!"

Boki laughed.

The trader's presence comforted Paulo. It was good to hear the affection in his voice. Olu was his friend and loved him, the boy knew full well. But Boki was his first true friend.

They settled to small talk and their evening meal. After a time, the two men drew aside and spoke alone. As night fell, light from the fire etched their faces like bronze masks in the darkness. Paulo could tell their talk was serious. Both seemed to have forgotten his presence. Now and again, he heard mention of the chief Kuokoa's name. He wondered why

Boki had come all the way to Manoa, since it was obvious he had not come to take the boy away.

All this talking and thinking tired Paulo. For now, it was enough that the trader had come. Olu suggested that he go to sleep.

Paulo said goodnight to all, and slipped quietly through the curtain. Perhaps tomorrow they'll tell me why Boki came, he thought as his eyes grew heavy.

When Paulo awoke the next morning, he found that the trader already had left the house. The boy went outside to join Olu who was busy at the cooking oven.

"Boki went to see the chief Kuokoa," the chant-maker told him.

"He came for that?" Paulo asked as they ate their morning poi and smoked fish.

"Yes," Olu said. "Kuokoa sent me to bring the trader to Manoa."

This was odd news! "I wonder why?" Paulo asked.

The big man paused in his meal to glance up, then veiled his eyes. "One can't be sure," he said. "The chief didn't tell me."

Paulo caught the evasion. "You think you know?" he asked.

"Perhaps."

The boy waited. He knew that usually Olu was quite willing to talk about the chief.

"What, then?" the boy asked.

Olu dodged the issue. "Aia! Always you ask questions! Boki will say when he's ready. Now tell me about the owl."

Paulo thought of something.

"My throwing stone! I left it tangled about the great owl. Someone in the chief's house must have found it!"

"Yes. The chief himself has it," Olu said.

Paulo was filled with consternation.

"The chief has it? You're sure?"

"Yes."

"Will I get it back?"

"That's for the chief to say. I think he'll return it. He won't keep a small boy's belongings."

Paulo was not so sure of this. He was deeply concerned over possible loss of his treasure.

"It's mine! I want it!" he said. His round cheeks grew flushed with anger. "He's a hateful chief!" Paulo stormed. "He ignores me, won't say I stay or go! And now he has my throwing stone. You must tell him I want it right away!"

Olu was aghast at the idea. "I . . . tell the chief? Surely your light head is talking!"

Paulo knew he was asking the impossible. Olu could never go to the chief with such a request. It was silly to have asked the chantmaker to do such a thing. He could get into serious trouble. But the boy felt so helpless.

"I . . . I'm sorry, Olu," he said. "Nothing seems to go right."

The big man's eyes grew serious, his deep voice gentle with understanding; "Have patience, little one," he said. "You'll have your throwing stone, I'm sure of it. Perhaps Boki will bring it when he comes from the chief."

Paulo realized there was nothing he could do but wait.

CHAPTER TWENTY-ONE

The Interview

BOKI had been more upset than he cared to show when Paulo greeted him with his outburst. He was troubled by the boy's obvious unhappiness. It was strange that the chief Kuokoa had not provided a home in the village, he thought. Boki had been so sure Paulo would be welcome. Because Kuokoa had lost his own son only a year ago, he should be sympathetic to the homeless boy, Boki felt.

Deeply troubled, the trader approached the main entrance to the chief's courtyard. A guard stood in the way, long spear clutched tightly across his breast.

"Kapu!" the man grunted. "None may pass!"

Boki halted, respectfully.

"The chief Kuokoa summoned me," he said.

"Who, then?"

"Boki, the trader. From Kou."

"Wait, then!"

The guard strode across the short distance to the house of the chief and announced the trader. Then he returned to accompany Boki to the steps of the porch. Kuokoa came out of the doorway, a smile of greeting on his face.

The trader bowed to the ground.

"Rise!" Kuokoa said, mildly. "We need not be formal."

"I have come as you ordered, Great One," the trader said.

Kuokoa looked frankly into Boki's eyes. "I have called you to come all this way," he explained, "because you may hold the key to a mystery."

Boki stood straight before the chief, completely at ease. He was used to the ways of the royal ones and knew they appreciated directness and straight answers.

"Recently, you sent a boy keiki to this village. In the company of Olu, our chantmaker."

"That is true, Great One."

Kuokoa looked at the trader, keenly. "Why?" he asked, abruptly.

Boki returned the chief's look, a tiny smile playing at the corners of his thin lips. "Aha! I wasn't wrong, then," he thought, swiftly. "He is interested in Paulo . . . a spark glows here. I have but to fan it!" Aloud, he said:

"The boy was homeless, Great One. His village and people were destroyed by renegade warriors from the south."

Kuokoa shook his head; the grey at his temples

flashing like silver in the morning sun. "All that I know!" he said. "But why send him here to Manoa?"

The trader lowered his eyes. "All know the Great One has a kind heart! I but thought . . ."

Kuokoa frowned. "Enough!" he said. "Let us save the pretty speeches. You must have had good reason to bring him so far. This matter presses my mind. What, exactly, do you know about the boy?"

Boki was puzzled.

"Know, Great One? I know he comes of honest family and a small but worthy village. I know his father died when the keiki was very young. I never heard his name."

Kuokoa glanced to one side, casually.

"Did you— You knew his mother?" he asked, softly.

Boki's brow puckered. "For years I have traded on that island, and gone to Paulo's village many times. Yet I scarcely noticed the boy's mother. Many considered her beautiful, I think."

"You knew her name?"

"No, Great One. But Paulo does, naturally." The trader thought: "Why doesn't he ask the boy such a question? To what is he leading? I must be careful here!"

Kuokoa persisted: "I meant, do you know anything of her family? Was she born on that island or did she come from afar?"

"I know the answers to none of those questions, Great One. Yet . . . I do recall she seemed much alone, stayed apart from the rest of the villagers. As though she grieved!"

Kuokoa sighed, deeply.

"I was afraid you would know little," he said.

Boki tried to read from the chief's expression what was on his mind. Certainly, there was a mystery here! He tried to further Paulo's cause.

"The boy is a brave little one, and he—"

Kuokoa stopped him with a kindly gesture. A slight smile raised his lips. "That he has already proved!" he said. "Wait!" He turned to enter the house, then returned with something in his hand. "You gave the boy this?" he asked, handing Paulo's throwing stone to the trader.

Mystified, Boki held the stone slackly in his palm.

"Yes, Great One," he agreed. "It was my parting gift to the boy."

The chief's hand trembled.

"Where did you get it?" he asked.

"From Paulo's village. I found it in the ashes, wrapped carefully in a piece of printed kapa. No one was alive to claim it, so—since the boy was the only one left in the village, I thought he should have it. It is rare, I think." He looked down at the stone. "And valuable!"

Kuokoa's deep-set eyes bored in. "Had the keiki never seen it? Didn't he recognize it on sight?"

"No, Great One. My gift was a complete surprise. He was delighted."

The chief's sternness lessened. "It must have been treasured all these years!" he said, wistfully.

"Eh? You recognize it, then?" Boki asked with surprise.

Kuokoa nodded.

"I saw it many years ago. It belonged to a son of the king of the big island. The son died on Maui! My own cousin, he was."

Boki's jaw dropped with astonishment. "King of the big island!" he thought in wonder. Aloud, he said, "If the stone belonged to the son of a king, I had no idea!" he hastened to assure the chief.

Kuokoa seemed to have forgotten the trader's presence. A sudden gust of warm trade wind ruffled his hair. Absently, he ran slender fingers through it.

"To think," he said, "it has come all this way to save the life of my youngest keiki. A powerful destiny must have guided it—surely the soul of a god dwells in this cold stone."

He reached to stroke the object in Boki's hand.

"There's no doubt it is the one. Mystic carvings . . . rare lava from the highest slopes of the volcano . . . human hair braided . . . all proclaim it genuine. And the gods chose this keiki, this particular boy, to wield it! It's amazing, a true miracle!"

"I was told of the owl's attack," Boki ventured to say.

"Aue! It might have been a double tragedy," Kuokoa said as he roused himself. "However, there is yet another matter. It concerns the boy's necklace."

Boki's eyes widened.

"The carved shell necklace?" he asked. "The one Paulo wears?"

"Does the necklace belong to the boy, or did you give that also?" Kuokoa asked.

"Of course it's his! Since birth he has worn it!" Boki thought rapidly. He was alarmed by all this questioning. "Paulo told me so himself, and I believe him, Great One. That boy does not lie!"

"I have reason to know this is true," Kuokoa agreed. "I was but making certain the necklace was actually his, not a gift from you."

"It is so!" Boki said with certainty. "The boy's mother gave it to the keiki."

The chief fingered his chin.

"The carved throwing stone and the necklace carved with the true love's verse!" he mused. "The Kahuna has proclaimed the necklace genuine! After examining it with great care, of course. It could not be by accident that these two things should come to Manoa at the same time!"

Kuokoa had moved away to the furthest end of the porch as he spoke. While the trader waited, the chief was lost in thought. It was not clear to Boki, even now, why he had been called. The chief seemed to recognize both the throwing stone and the necklace. That they had something to do with Paulo, was obvious. But what was the chief so interested in establishing? Boki did not know. He felt momentous things were in the making.

A servant appeared at the curtain of the chief's house. He roused Kuokoa from his thinking and after a low-voiced conversation, withdrew. Kuokoa stood facing Boki.

"Thank you for coming so speedily," he said, graciously. "You have helped me more than you could know. A grave matter must be settled here. It involves the boy. I felt I must learn what you could tell me."

"I am honored to be of service, Great One," Boki said. He fingered the throwing stone in his hand. "Shall I return this to Paulo?"

Kuokoa reached to take it from the trader's grasp. "No. I shall return it with proper thanks," he said. "The boy has done me a great service. He should have his reward from my lips."

"True, Great One. It will please the boy. He has become unhappy in the village, feeling he is not wanted in Manoa!"

This was a daring thing to say to the chief. But Boki was not satisfied with the interview. Much had been hinted and nothing said, he felt. The chief was not speaking his mind, truly. Boldly, the trader took the opportunity to try and help Paulo.

Kuokoa reacted surprisingly. "The boy is unhappy?" he asked, sternly. "Has anyone dared to harm him? They will be punished! I gave strict orders the keiki was to be cared for properly!"

"None have done him real harm, Great One," Boki explained. "It's just that the boy is lonely. Time is endless at his age. He realizes he has no home. No family. He has waited word from the chief."

Kuokoa frowned. It was apparent that he was conscious of his own delay. "True . . . the young are impatient," he said. "Like worms in a green nut.

Very well, Paulo shall have his answer tomorrow. When the sun is at its highest. Tell Olu to bring the keiki to my court for a formal hearing."

He smiled, graciously.

"You also seemed to have questions in your eyes as we spoke!" His own eyes twinkled as he watched Boki's embarrassed flush. "You may come with them," he added, then waved a hand of dismissal. "Meanwhile I must think."

Boki bowed low and backed from the chief's presence.

"He is cagey, that one!" the trader told himself. "Now what . . . exactly . . . do I know?"

CHAPTER TWENTY-TWO

The Chief Tells a Story

PAULO sat on one uncomfortable rock after another. Worried about a lot of things, he waited for Boki to return from his talk with the chief. It seemed to the boy that the trader was gone a long time. "I wish Boki would hurry!" he told himself.

In spite of a large bowl of poi, he was still hungry. He stripped off a ripe banana from a bunch lying on its side near the cooking oven. He ate this, then took another. Now that his cuts were healing, his appetite was hard to satisfy. After a time, Paulo saw the trader striding up the path toward Olu's new thatched house. The boy slipped off the rock and limped to meet his friend.

"You have my throwing stone?" he asked. But a glance at Boki's hands showed them empty. "I knew the chief would keep it!" he added, trying to swallow his disappointment.

The trader slowed his stride as he approached the rock.

"Not so!" he answered. "Kuokoa will return it tomorrow."

"Why tomorrow?"

"So that he may thank you properly."

Paulo was surprised. "The chief was pleased?" he asked.

"Why not? You saved his keiki from the owl!"

Paulo thought this over. True, the chief should be grateful, but why this delay?

They joined Olu at the cooking oven. Paulo watched as the trader seated himself near the pile of firewood.

"You were gone a time," Olu said, casually.

Paulo leaned against a rock to pick at dry moss in a crack. It was pleasant here on high ground where soft breezes fanned the cheek. Olu's new house was built in a good spot. However, Paulo was not thinking of this. "They both know of something they will not tell me," he decided. "That's why Boki came." He was unhappy, realizing there was a thing they would not say in his presence.

Boki chuckled as he settled his lean frame.

"It seems we are to go to the chief," he said, importantly.

"You just came from him!" Olu protested.

"I mean all of us!"

"All? You mean Paulo and me, too?"

"The chief holds a formal hearing in the big house!"

Olu dropped his prodding stick, and a sooty rock rolled back into the cooking oven.

"Aia!" he said. "Something's afoot!"

Boki agreed. "Much may come of it, I think! We had a queer meeting."

"Can you tell us?" Olu asked.

"There's little to tell. The chief bides his time."

Paulo was not sure he had heard aright. To stand before the chief in his royal court! He was too awed to imagine such a thing. An appalling idea came to him.

"He's going to send me away!" Paulo said, lips trembling.

"You talk like a fish with no bones," Boki chided. "The chief said nothing like that!"

"What did he say, then?" Paulo demanded.

The trader looked away in confusion. "It was man talk!" he said.

And Paulo had to be satisfied with that.

For the rest of the day it seemed to the boy that Boki and Olu both avoided him, were always deep in secret conversation. Paulo strayed off by himself to do some serious thinking. It was like a walk around the taro patch—he came right back where he started from. Air seemed dead and motionless; leaves hung like weighted fingers from the trees. Even sounds were muted in a mind dulled by too much using.

And the next morning was worse than before as

Paulo watched the round disk of sun and counted hours until it was time to go to the chief's court. Olu's wife, had brought both the chantmaker and Paulo clean loincloths specially printed with her most attractive designs, black arrow heads and brilliant red squares with brown centers. The chantmaker had scrubbed the boy until his skin felt as raw as a scaled fish!

When Paulo protested, Olu spanked him with a flat palm, jokingly.

"You disgrace my new house!" he said.

Paulo's lips grimaced. "I couldn't get clean with all these bandages," he defended himself.

"We look," Olu said. "Perhaps you are healed. Aia, the trouble you cause me!"

With gentle fingers, the big man unwound all the wrappings. Healing leaves and a salve of clay had done their work well.

"All pau, you think? Olu asked the trader as the unsightly scratches were uncovered.

Boki stopped splashing his face and chest long enough to come take a look.

"What a mauling the keiki took," the trader said, compassionately. "Let me see. You were very brave, little one!"

Carefully, they looked over all the cuts and scratches.

"Some are healed," Boki said. "But not all."

"Then we take no chances. More bandages," Olu said.

Paulo was tired of his bindings. "Small ones!" he pleaded.

"Not so many this time," Olu agreed.

Word of the royal hearing had been told from mouth to mouth. Everyone in the village wondered why these three had been summoned. All in the village square stopped to watch as they filed down the path.

Paulo felt very grown up as he walked between the two men. Few villagers ever saw the inside of the chief's court, and excitement helped the boy to keep from thinking of his fear. Now that the time had arrived, Paulo did not know what he wanted the chief Kuokoa to decide. Boki's presence in Manoa changed everything. It would be much easier if the trader took him away, the boy felt. However, he must get back his throwing stone, whatever the chief said.

The royal flag was whipping in the trade wind at the top of its tall pole. Two guards in formal dress met them at the entrance. They wore crested helmets, short feathered shoulder capes, and carried long spears. No one else was in sight, but Paulo could hear the murmur of many voices from inside the long house where the chief's court was to be held. When they approached the wide doorway, Paulo faltered.

"I'm afraid," he whispered.

"Courage, little one," both men prompted.

They filed through the entrance. Immediately, the guards warned them to kneel. Foreheads touched the ground. Olu's broad back prevented Paulo from catching sight of the chief. He wanted to raise his head and steal a look, then decided he had better not.

"Rise and bow to your chief!" the guard said.

Kuokoa, mighty chief of the village of Manoa, was seated on woven mats of finest texture, raised high on a platform of polished black stone. A red, crested helmet of rich feather-work crowned his stern brow. A long yellow-feathered cloak reached below his knees. A resplendent feathered loincloth bound his waist while its skirt flaps covered his lap. Freshly strung flowers formed many fragrant garlands about his neck and shoulders.

On each side of the chief stood tall, haughty guards. The chief's sharp battle spears, outrigger canoe paddles, and other special possessions were arranged in an impressive display behind the throne. Large stone lamps filled with kukuinut oil gave spluttering yellow light in the dim interior. Even his magnificently polished war canoe was placed on display across one end of the room.

Stewards of the chief, tax gatherers, and members of his royal household sat in the flickering glow at some distance from the throne. The Kahuna, in full priestly regalia stood at one side of the chief, his wrinkled face set in an expressionless mask.

To the boy born and raised in a very small village, the chief's court was a magnificent sight. If Boki and Olu were not present, Paulo knew he could not face the chief. With eyes staring at him from all sides, he stood as though in a trance.

A soft drum roll sounded as one of the attendants touched fingers to taut sharkskin stretched on a fat gourd. Shuffling ceased throughout the long room. Only then did the chief speak.

"Let the boy, Paulo, step forward!" Kuokoa ordered in a deep, coldly formal voice. "My words concern him."

Paulo felt Olu's hand give a prompting shove. Shakily, he moved to stand directly in front of the chief in the center of the gathering. Perspiration dampened his palms. His knees felt stiff and clumsy. He hardly dared raise his eyes.

Kuokoa glanced about the court.

"This keiki was brought to Manoa, seeking a home," he said. "All know of his unhappy plight. I must decide whether he stays and who shall adopt him."

The chief paused and stared directly into the boy's large eyes.

"Paulo," he said. "I have pondered your problem overlong. Filled with doubts and needing proof of certain things, I kept you waiting. Now you shall have your answer."

Paulo's slender body stiffened.

"But first I must tell you a story," the chief added.

Paulo hardly dared to breathe.

A far look came into the chief's eyes. "Many years ago," he began. "Before I came to Manoa, I lived with my uncle the great king of the big island called Hawaii. At that time my cousin, a royal prince by the name of Moku, was in love with Hokulani, a beautiful princess of the court. The king had promised Hokulani to another man," the chief said, softly.

"My cousin was determined to have the princess

for his own. He fled with her to the island of Maui. Here, they married. A certain chief on Maui was jealous of their presence, fearing the royal prince would seek to rule the island. So, he ambushed and slew my cousin Moku."

Kuokoa's face grew sad.

"The beautiful princess was taken away and hidden in a small village by the sea. Here in near poverty, she lived with the villagers. None knew she was a royal one, since she was silenced by threat of death."

The chief paused. It was apparent the story caused him pain. Paulo wondered where all this was leading.

"Meanwhile," Kuokoa went on, "the King of Hawaii felt betrayed. In his wrath, he threatened instant death by the spear to any who spoke the names of the lost couple. The other man, the one who had been chosen by the king to wed the princess, undertook a secret search for Moku and Hokulani. By the time this man traced the pair to the island of Maui, he found he was too late."

Kuokoa drew a deep breath.

"The wicked chief on Maui claimed that Moku had died in battle, and said the princess had died, too, of the plague. Afraid to return home and face the king's displeasure, the heartsick man paddled north in his great canoe to settle on the larger island of Oahu. After a time, this man's sadness over losing both cousin and promised bride was healed. He married and raised a family of his own . . . became chief to the King of Oahu . . . and prospered."

The chief seemed lost in his story. Paulo watched as Kuokoa glanced unseeingly around the room. A nervous shuffling moved the crowd; guards stiffened their long spears as though in warning.

"I was that man," Kuokoa said almost in a whisper. "And the sad experience of losing both cousin and well-loved princess was long in healing. Yet in time this tragedy of my youth was forgotten . . ."

Kuokoa raised a slender hand to point toward Paulo.

"Forgotten . . . until this young boy came to Manoa!"

CHAPTER TWENTY-THREE

A Startling Disclosure

PAULO could feel all eyes staring at the back of his neck. When Kuokoa resumed speaking, his voice was stronger.

"This homeless boy from a small village on Maui, came to us one year from the death of my dear son." His eyes lifted. "Indeed, the gods must have sent him!"

Kuokoa reached a hand beneath his cloak to draw forth Paulo's throwing stone. Holding it aloft for all to see, he said in a loud voice:

"This pikoi belonged to my cousin, Moku!"

He gestured toward Paulo.

"This boy brought it with him. With the throwing stone he snared the vicious owl and saved my youngest keiki's life!"

He pointed at Paulo's throat.

"This same boy wears a strand of carved shell around his neck. A love token given to his mother, Hokulani, by me!"

Kuokoa rose, suddenly, to stand before his throne.

"Paulo is of royal blood, son of the lost princess Hokulani. I will swear it!" he said.

A gasp of wonder went the rounds of the assembly. Whispered questions filled the air. Guards stamped the butts of their spears to the ground to bring order.

Paulo was astounded. He tried to comprehend what the chief was saying, but his wits were muddled. Seated now, Kuokoa raised an imperious hand.

"Attend me!" he said. "I demand that all honors be paid this boy! He is a royal one, protected by the gods!"

Tears glistened on the chief's lashes as he looked directly at Paulo. "Come!" he beckoned.

Excited and overcome with surprise, Paulo was close to tears. Bashfully, he approached the chief's throne.

Pride filled Kuokoa's voice as he announced:

"I take this boy, Paulo, as my adopted son—my eldest keiki!"

A hearty cheer filled the court. All present were delighted. The Kahuna nodded his head as with a palsy, looking smug and knowing. Smiling with happiness, Kuokoa raised both arms toward the stunned boy.

"Sit here, by my knee!" he commanded.

When Paulo had seated himself gingerly on the

very edge, his eyes sought Olu and Boki. The trader's face was wreathed in a warm smile of approval. Olu's big jaw was sagged, his face pale and radiant with wonder. Paulo tried to gather his wits. "They're as much surprised as I," he told himself.

He snuggled against the feathers of the chief's cloak. They were soft and luxurious, as he had imagined. He looked up at Kuokoa. A broad smile brightened the chief's features. Paulo had never seen him look so warm and friendly. He seemed a new man, a stranger to the strict and forbidding presence he knew.

Kuokoa raised a hand for silence, motioning to one of his stewards:

"Bring the royal attire!" he commanded.

He looked fondly down at Paulo. "You're of a size with my lost son—the fit should be perfect!"

When the steward stepped forward, he held out a complete duplicate of the chief's costume—a feathered cape in the same design as Kuokoa's, yellow and green with streaks of red like flashes of lightning down its back, a soft loincloth with feathered waist band and loin flaps, and a proud crested helmet covered with red feathers of most brilliant hue.

"Feathers of the O-o bird!" Paulo exclaimed, remembering the black bird which had perched so jauntily atop the olona bush on his walk from the plains of Kou. Here were the same pale yellow tufts from the O-o's precious wings!

In full sight of the assembly, Paulo was dressed in the royal costume of a chief's son.

Unconsciously, his head was held high. Paulo felt inches taller in the resplendent helmet. His small waist felt snug in the soft loincloth. Everything fit. "All these are to be my own!" he thought, hardly daring to believe it.

"Like a true warrior you look!" Kuokoa said, well pleased. "It becomes you! You have your mother's dear features."

To the assembly, he said:

"Proper ceremonies will be held by the Kahuna. Blessings and thanks to the gods will be given. A great feast will be held this evening to do honor to my new son. All Manoa will attend to pay their respects and give homage to the Royal One. Two fat black pigs already are roasting in the royal ovens. Let my command be obeyed!"

He drew Paulo to him.

"Now little one, what have you to say?"

It was as though Paulo was caught fast in one of his own extravagant day dreams. Only one practical thought would come:

"Please, Great One," he asked. "Could I have my throwing stone?"

Kuokoa chuckled.

"With my deepest gratitude," he said, handing the smooth handle to the boy. "It belongs to a true hunter!"

With trembling fingers, Paulo wrapped the braided cord and stuck the precious talisman into his loincloth. Now he felt better!

"I would . . . like to be a hunter, Great One!" Paulo said. "And . . . and a good son!"

"Already, you are a brave and skilled thrower of the stone!" Kuokoa answered. "And the spear!" he added with a laugh. "A true royal one. Other things

I will teach you, my dear son. But you owned these things. Is there nothing else you want?"

It was really then that Paulo realized what a miraculous thing had happened. He knew for certain that he was to stay in Manoa!

And the chief had proclaimed him as his true adopted son—he would have a father like other boys. But . . . where was he to live? Undoubtedly, he would have to leave Olu's new house. The thought was disturbing. The possibility of being separated from Olu and Boki filled Paulo with dismay. He loved them both!

"Must . . . must I leave Olu?" he asked Kuokoa. "And . . . must Boki go?"

Kuokoa must have sensed the boy's dilemma. He raised a hand for silence.

"Hear me!" he said to all assembled. "Olu, Chantmaker to the King, attend! Boki, known to all as The Trader, attend! It is my royal decree that henceforth, both of these men may visit my new son and my house without kapu. Olu shall be Paulo's personal guard and counsellor. Both men are under the royal protection of my hand. Death to any man who disobeys this command!"

To Paulo, he said:

"You will live in my house. Some day you'll have one of your own. Meanwhile, you eat from my cooking oven."

Great happiness filled Paulo's heart.

Everything was settled—the decision made.

Beside him sat his new father. His throwing stone was returned. The necklace given by his mother was indeed a true talisman. His sleeping mats would belong in the chief's house. Olu would be his well-loved companion, to sing chants in the forest and on the sea. And hadn't Boki, his true friend, promised in Kou that he would return often to the island? Also, the boy knew now that his dream of being a hunter would be realized.

Paulo laughed aloud! Joyously . . . with relief and great happiness.

Kuokoa threw back his head and laughed too! He hugged Paulo close as Olu and Boki stood proudly watching. Happy grins spread across their faces from ear to ear. Paulo felt what a wonderful thing it was to be wanted, and to live in the valley called Manoa.

SOME HAWAIIAN WORDS AND THEIR MEANINGS

NOTE: In Hawaiian, all the vowels are sounded separately. As for example: aia . . . pronounced, ah, ee, yah!

aia . . . an exclamation of surprise.

aloha . . . greetings; love; welcome; farewell.

aloha nui . . . a big greeting, etc.

aloha oe . . . a very personal greeting to a friend.

aue . . . alas!, a lament.

imu . . . a cooking oven or pit.

kahuna . . . a powerful holy man, priest.

kapa . . . pounded tapa bark cloth.

kapu . . . forbidden.

kauwa . . . slave.

keiki . . . child. (Keiki wahine, girl. Keiki kani, boy.)

kona . . . wind from the big island, Hawaii. (All bad weather.)

kukui . . . a native nut, like a black walnut.

kulolo . . . taro root and coconut pudding.

lauhala . . . matting woven from pandanus tree leaves.

luau . . . a feast or party.

manu pueo . . . a native owl.

mele . . . a chant, either spoken or sung.

nui . . . large, great. (Added to other words, as; opu nui, etc.)

ohia . . . a very hard native wood, violet in color.

olona . . . a nettle bush; fibers used in fishlines, etc.

opu . . . stomach, abdomen.

pandanus . . . a tree with long, swordlike, fibrous leaves.

pahoehoe . . . smooth lava.

pau . . . all done; finished; no more.

pili . . . a long, native grass . . . now extinct.

pikoi . . . a throwing stone with a long cord and handle.

pilikia . . . trouble!

piko . . . a sacred tuft of grass over doorways.

poi . . . pounded taro root; a pasty form of native bread.

taro . . . a root plant used in food.

ti . . . a low plant with long, wide leaves . . . used as wrappings.

wiliwili . . . a very light wood, like balsa wood.